CONTENTS

EDITIONS

The following editions have been published

FIRST EDITION   Issued in 1919.

SECOND EDITION   Issued in 1926.

THIRD EDITION   Issued in 1939.
                     Supplement issued, 1947.
                     Reprinted incorporating Supplement, 1954.

FOURTH EDITION   Issued in 1961.

FIFTH EDITION   Issued in 1972.
                     Reprinted with amendments, 1985.

SIXTH EDITION   Issued in 1990.

CONSTITUTION OF COMMITTEE

SHIPS and OFFSHORE REGULATIONS COMMITTEE

Constitution as at January 1989

The President   (*ex officio*)   J K Robinson
D M Carlisle   (Chairman)   D St.J Seigne
                                            E E Simpson

and   *nominated by*

Appointment Pending	Association of Offshore Diving Contractors
M R Desmond ⎫	BEAMA Ltd
G E Woodliff ⎭	
A Kynaston ⎫	
J Ward ⎬	British Cable Makers' Confederation
P Waterworth ⎭	
F Parr	British Marine Equipment Council
R L F Smith	British Rig Owners' Association
L T Barclay	British Shipbuilders
A W Gilbey	British Telecom
E J Gorse	Department of Energy
T A D Sharp	Department of Transport (Marine Directorate)
J Osmond	Electrical Contractors' Association
G H Turnbull	Electrical Contractors' Association of Scotland
Appointment pending	Electronic Engineering Association
G Clare	Engineering Equipment & Materials Users' Association
E Ellwood	General Council of British Shipping
H Rush	Institute of Marine Engineers
S C Williams	Institute of Petroleum
M J Gosling	Institution of Electrical & Electronics Incorporated Engineers
Appointment pending	Institution of Engineers & Shipbuilders in Scotland
I F Davies	Lighting Industry Federation
F D S McCrudden	Lloyd's Register of Shipping
L Powell	Ministry of Defence (Sea Systems Controllerate)
W M Somerville	North East Coast Institution of Engineers & Shipbuilders
A Evans	Oil Industry International Exploration & Production Forum
T R Foster	UK Offshore Operators Association
B Kitchen ⎫	Co-opted Members
J D McIver ⎭	

INTRODUCTION

The Sixth Edition supersedes as from its date of issue, (June 1990), all previous editions of the "Regulations for the Electrical and Electronic Equipment of Ships".

Only proved materials, appliances and methods are considered, but it is not intended to discourage invention or to exclude other materials, appliances and methods which may be proved in the future. The Council of the Institution of Electrical Engineers may add to or modify the "Recommended Practice" from time to time as may in their opinion be necessary to provide for the use of additional methods, materials or appliances.

SCOPE

These "Regulations" and "Recommended Practice" apply to the electrical equipment for the generation, storage, conversion, distribution and utilisation of electrical energy for all purposes in ships of all descriptions except ships of war and include, where relevant, inland and harbour craft. They are designed to provide safety of installed equipment, and portable and transportable equipment intended to be connected to the ship's distribution system, especially from fire, shock and burns, and to facilitate the satisfactory operation of such equipment.

The "Regulations" and "Recommended Practice" relate principally to requirements for the installation, utilisation, inspection and testing but certain requirements for the construction of electrical and electronic equipment are included.

The "Recommended Practice", except for references to Standards, does not relate to the internal wiring of manufactured apparatus which is not wired on board. It is not intended to provide for every circumstance — those of a special character may require the advice of a specialist.

PART 1

REGULATIONS

for the

ELECTRICAL and ELECTRONIC EQUIPMENT

of SHIPS

REGULATIONS FOR THE ELECTRICAL AND ELECTRONIC EQUIPMENT OF SHIPS

1. Good workmanship and the use of proper materials are essential for compliance with these Regulations.

2. All electrical equipment shall be constructed, installed and protected and shall be capable of being maintained, inspected and tested, so as to prevent danger so far as is reasonably practicable.

3. Except where a specific statement is made to the contrary, all Regulations are equally applicable to a.c. and d.c. installations.

4. Materials, appliances, accessories and fittings, etc., shall comply with the relevant British Standards or acceptable International or National Standards in so far as they are applicable. Where special marine type apparatus is required, any special features involving departure from a generally applicable British, International or National Standard shall not impair the safety of the installation or of personnel.

5. The design, construction and installation of all electrical equipment shall be compatible with the conditions of marine service.

6. All electrical conductors shall be:

(i) of sufficient size and current rating for the purposes for which they are used,

(ii) insulated, secured and protected as to prevent danger.

7. All apparatus shall be suitable for the maximum power demanded of it when it is in use. It shall be so constructed, installed and protected as to prevent danger.

8. Installations are to be protected against accidental overcurrents including short-circuits. The protective devices are to provide complete and co-ordinated protection to ensure:

(i) continuity of service under fault conditions through discriminative action of protective devices so far as is practicable,

(ii) elimination of the fault so as to reduce damage to the system and hazard of fire.

9. Adequate precautions shall be taken to ensure continuity of services the failure of which would hazard the ship.

10. In the design and installation of electric apparatus, precautions shall be taken to ensure that, should the primary insulation become defective, the danger from electric shock is reduced to a minimum.

11. Every electrical connection shall be of proper construction regarding conductance, insulation, mechanical strength and protection.

12. Effective means shall be provided so that all voltage may be cut off from each and every circuit and sub-circuit and from all apparatus as may be necessary to prevent danger.

13. All conductors and apparatus liable to be exposed to flammable or explosive atmospheres shall be so constructed and protected and such special precautions shall be taken as to prevent danger.

14. The primary source of electrical power and any necessary transforming apparatus shall be provided with reserve capacity such that failure of any part of it does not prevent the use of essential services.

15. The operating voltage of portable tools and similar equipment shall be such as to prevent danger in areas where risk from electric shock is high.

16. All relevant Statutory requirements, see Part 2, are to be complied with.

PART 2

UNITED KINGDOM
STATUTORY REQUIREMENTS
and OTHER
RELEVANT GUIDANCE

UNITED KINGDOM STATUTORY REQUIREMENTS AND OTHER RELEVANT GUIDANCE

1.   Statutory requirements

Of the Statutory requirements which apply where a ship is to be registered under the United Kingdom Merchant Shipping Act 1894, the following Statutory Instruments made under that and subsequent Merchant Shipping Acts have technical relevance to electrical installations:

Statutory Instrument No.	Title	References of Special Interest
1.1	Construction and equipment	
(1) 1980 No. 543	Merchant Shipping (Pilot Ladders and Hoists) Regulations	Regulation 8(2)(1)
(2) 1984 No. 1216	Merchant Shipping (Passenger Ship Construction & Survey) Regulations	42-54 inclusive, 56(4) and (5), and 67 (see Note 1)
(3) 1984 No. 1217	Merchant Shipping (Cargo Ship Construction & Survey) Regulations	Regulations 13(3), 14(4), 15(5), 24, 32-41 inclusive, 42-50 inclusive (See Note 2)
(4) 1986 No.1067	Merchant Shipping (Cargo Ship Construction & Survey) Regulations 1984 (Amendment) Regulations	Regulation 4
(5) 1987 No. 549	Merchant Shipping (IBC Code) Regulations	Regulation 3 (See Note 3)
(6) 1986 No.1073	Merchant Shipping (Gas Carriers) Regulations	Regulation 3 (See Note 3)
(7) 1987 No. 1886	Merchant Shipping (Passenger Ship Construction) (Amendment) Regulations 1987	Regulation 3

NOTE 1   The electrical equipment and installation required by Regulation 43 of SI 1984 No.1216 shall comply with the requirements specified in the current Merchant Shipping Notice relevant to that Regulation.

NOTE 2   The electrical equipment and installations required by Regulation 42 of SI 1984 No.1217 shall comply with the requirements specified in the current Merchant Shipping Notice relevant to that Regulation.

NOTE 3   Where appropriate, these Regulations require compliance with the following International Maritime Organisation (IMO) publications:

International Code for the Construction and Equipment of Ships Carrying Dangerous Chemicals in Bulk (IBC)   Regulations   3.7.8, 3.7.10,   10.1 to 10.4 inclusive,   15.3.10, 15.11.5 and 15.15

International Code for Construction and Equipment of Ships Carrying Liquified Gases in Bulk (IGC)   Regulations 1.3, 3.6, 10.1 to 10.2.5.4 inclusive, 12.1.9, 12.1.10 and 17.2

1.2   Fire and life-saving

(1)   1984 No. 1218 Merchant Shipping (Fire Protection) Regulations   Regulations 70(1) and (2), 89, Schedule 7(6) and (8)
Schedule 8(6)
Schedule 10(3)(b)(iii) and (3)(c)
Schedule   11(1)(b) and (c),   (2)(f) and (3)(a)
Schedule 12(1)(c) and (d) and (2)(a)

(2)   1986 No.1066   Merchant Shipping (Life-Saving Appliances) Regulations   Regulations 15(4) and (5) and 18(8)

1.3   Radio and navigational equipment

(1)   1974 No. 1919 Merchant Shipping (Radio) (Fishing Vessels) Rules   Rules 4 and 5

(2)   1980 No. 529   Merchant Shipping (Radio) (Installations) Regulations   Regulations   6(1), 11(1) and (3), 14(4) and (5), 17(1) and (3), 22(g) and (h) and 25

(3)   1984 No. 1203   Merchant Shipping (Navigational Equipment) Regulations   Regulations 5, 6 and 7

1.4   Crew accommodation

1978 No. 795	Merchant Shipping (Crew Accommodation) Regulations	Regulations 7(6), 14(5), 15(4), (5) and (7), 16(6), 23(2)(c), 23(5)(j), 25(5)(b) and (g), Schedule 3, Schedule 4 para (7) and (11), Schedule 6 paras 8(5) and (6), Schedule 6 para 9(6) and Appendix 2 para 5

1.5   Fishing vessels

1975 No. 330	Fishing Vessels (Safety Provisions) Rules	Rules 34(3) and (9), 35(3), 38-43 inclusive and 116

1.6   Diving and submersibles

1981 No. 1098	Merchant Shipping (Submersible Craft Construction and Survey) Regulations	Schedule 1(2) and Schedule 2(2)

1.7   Dangerous goods and materials hazardous only in bulk

(1)   1981 No. 1747 Merchant Shipping (Dangerous Goods) Regulations

(2)   1986 No. 1069 Merchant Shipping (Dangerous Goods) (Amendment) Regulations

(3)   Where appropriate, these Regulations require compliance with:

(i)	Carriage of Dangerous Goods in Ships — Report of the Standing Advisory Committee 1978 — The "Blue Book" Fourth Edition 1984 as amended	Class 1 Section 1 paras 5.3.6 to 5.3.9 inclusive.
(ii)	IMO Code of Safe Practice for solid cargoes (see also 5.1)	Appendix B

1.8   The above Statutory Instruments and "Blue Book" may be obtained from Her Majesty's Stationery Office (HMSO), 51 Nine Elms Lane, London, U.K. SW8 5DR.

Merchant Shipping Notices may be obtained from the Marine Library, Sunley House, 90-93 High Holborn, London, U.K. WC1V 6LP.

The above IMO publications may be obtained from the International Maritime Organisation, 4 Albert Embankment, London, U.K. SE1 7SR.

2. Where compliance with The Safety of Life at Sea Convention 1974 (SOLAS) and its Protocol of 1978 is required, the provisions of the Convention and its Protocol are embodied, where appropriate, in the Statutory Instruments listed in paragraph 1 of this Part.

3. While work is being carried out in harbour, compliance is required with the Health and Safety at Work etc. Act 1974. Sections 2, 3 and 6 have technical relevance to these Recommendations.

4. Instructions for the guidance of surveyors

The Instructions should be referred to for the following subjects:

> Survey of Passenger ships
> Survey of Fire Appliances
> Survey of Life-Saving Appliances
> Survey of Merchant Shipping Radio Installations
> Survey of Merchant Shipping Navigational Equipment Installations
> Survey of Crew Accommodation in Merchant Ships
> Survey of Lights and Signalling Equipment
> Survey of Fishing Vessels
> Survey of Submersible Craft*

> * Available from —
> Department of Transport, Publication Sales Unit, Building 1, Victoria Road, South Ruislip, Middlesex, U.K. RA4 0ZZ.

Other Instructions may be obtained from HMSO.

5. Other relevant guidance

5.1 The safe carriage of coal cargoes. Emission of flammable gases and spontaneous combustion. Merchant Shipping Notice No. M971.

5.2 Merchant Shipping Notice No. M752. Safety. Electric shock hazard in the use of electic arc welding plant. Obtainable from the Marine Library.

5.3 The Code of Practice for the safe use of electicity underwater (September 1985) published by the Association of Offshore Diving Contractors, 28-30 Little Russell Street, London, U.K. WC1A 2HN.

5.4 General requirements for marine navigational equipment 1982. Obtainable from HMSO.

5.5 Home Office code of practice for ships wire antenna systems for radiotelegraphy transmissions, MPT 1270. Obtainable from HMSO.

xviii

5.6 Programmable Electronic Systems in Safety Related Systems published by the Health and Safety Executive. Obtainable from HMSO.

5.7 Guidelines for the specification and operation of dynamically positioned diving support vessels (May 1983) issued by the Petroleum Engineering Division of the UK Department of of Energy and the Norwegian Petroleum Directorate. Obtainable from HMSO.

PART 3

RECOMMENDED PRACTICE

for the

implementation of the

REGULATIONS

for the

ELECTRICAL and ELECTRONIC EQUIPMENT

of SHIPS

SECTION 1

GENERAL REQUIREMENTS

General

1.1   This Section contains operating conditions and recommendations which are common to all apparatus and installations.

1.2   All apparatus should be of a design appropriate to the situation in which it is to be used and its mode of installation should take account of the conditions likely to be encountered in service. Examples of such conditions are:

   (i)   Exposure to moisture and salt laden atmosphere, sea spray, high wind velocity, ice formation.

   (ii) Exposure to abnormal vibration or shock.

   (iii) Exposure to excessively high or low temperatures.

   (iv) Exposure to explosive mixtures of gases, dusts and circumstances where there is an abnormal risk of fire or explosion.

1.3   These recommendations are applicable equally to a.c. and d.c. installations except where a specific statement is made to the contrary.

1.4   Voltage and frequency

(1)   All apparatus should function satisfactorily during sustained voltage fluctuations within 10% below or 6% above the rated voltage of the system and a.c. apparatus should function satisfactorily at frequencies within plus or minus 5% of the rated frequency of the system. The supply system should be arranged so that the transient conditions during starting of machines, etc., which are greater than those defined above will not cause maloperation of or damage to other equipment e.g.:

   (i)   where pole changing deck machinery is involved a dip of 15% and a recovery time of less than 0.2 second may be suitable;

   (ii) where pole changing deck machinery is not involved a dip of 15% and a recovery time of less than 1 second may be suitable.

     NOTE: Current harmonics, inter-acting with the impedance of the supply will generate voltage harmonics. Both the current and voltage harmonics can cause malfunction and overheating in other equipment in the ship if their possible presence has not been taken into account in the equipment design. For systems where a converter rating is large and a significant proportion of the system rating, it may not be feasible to suppress such

1

harmonics at source. Consequently, appropriate measures may have to be taken to attenuate these effects on critical equipment; such measures may include electrical isolation, (e.g. MG sets), filters in the supply to critical equipment, correct screening of cables and construction of enclosures, etc. General guidance is given in Appendix D.

(2)   Where non-linear loads such as saturated chokes and static inverters / converters, individually or collectively, form a significant proportion of the total electrical system of the ship, all necessary information regarding the harmonic voltage and current characteristics of such loads should be passed to the party responsible for the design of the ship's electrical system.

(3)   In circuits supplied by accumulator batteries the voltage variations given in (1) are likely to be exceeded, particularly where the battery is normally on floating service. The apparatus supplied should function satisfactorily within the maximum voltage fluctuations likely to be met in all operating conditions. Voltage variations of plus 30% and minus 25% as determined by the charging / discharging characteristics and the ripple voltage from the charging device, should be taken into account.

NOTE: Batteries supplying the emergency services required by SOLAS should be capable of carrying the emergency electrical load without recharging whilst maintaining the voltage of the battery throughout the discharge period within 12% above or below the rated voltage.

1.5   Electrical and electronic equipment which may operate under automatic or remote control should do so without risk of damage to plant or injury to personnel.

1.6   All conductors, switchgear and accessories should be capable of carrying, without damage, any current which may flow through them under all conditions.

1.7   Measures should be taken to ensure the satisfactory reception of radio signals for communication, navigation or other purpose. In order to achieve and maintain freedom from electromagnetic interference emanating from electrical and electronic equipment within the ship, all equipment should comply with the requirements of BS 1597 with regard to conducted and radiated interference levels.

1.8   No addition, temporary or permanent, should be made to the designed load of the existing installation until it has been definitely ascertained that the current carrying capacity and the conditions of the existing accessories, conductors, switchgear, etc., are adequate for the increased load.

1.9   Where these Recommendations call for the use of particular

2

materials, appliances and methods, the use of other materials, appliances and methods is admissible provided they are no less effective or reliable.

1.10   For the purpose of these Recommendations the following cooling-air and cooling-water temperatures are assumed.

(1)   For all ocean going ships and ships intended to operate within the tropical belt, i.e. between latitudes 35°N and 20°S:

(i)   Primary cooling-water supply.   30°C
In ships employing a centralised secondary cooling system, equipment should be rated for the specified cooling medium temperature of that system.

(ii)   Cooling-air temperature for equipment located in   45°C
machinery spaces or on weather decks.

(iii)   Cooling-air temperature for equipment located in all other   40°C
spaces.

(2)   For vessels such as coasters, ferries and harbour craft intended solely for use in Northern or Southern waters outside the tropical belt:

(i)   Primary cooling-water supply.   25°C
In ships employing a centralised secondary cooling system, equipment should be rated for the specified cooling medium temperature of that system.

(ii)   Cooling-air temperature in all situations   40°C

NOTE 1   The term cooling-air refers to the air responsible for dissipating the heat losses from the equipment or cables concerned. Allowance must be made for any increased temperature inside enclosures.

NOTE 2   Where equipment operates in ambient temperatures higher than the limits given in 1.10 e.g. in locations which may be subject to excessive heat such as boiler rooms and galleys, due allowance should be made in the rating of the equipment.

1.11   Inclination of ship

(1)   All machines and apparatus should operate satisfactorily under all conditions with the ship inclined up to the following angles from the normal:

Transversely	15° list;
or rolling up to	22° 30';
Longitudinally	10° trim.

(2)   Emergency machines and apparatus fitted in accordance with Statutory requirements for emergency plant should operate satisfactorily in addition when the ship is inclined 22° 30' and / or when the trim of the ship is 10° from the normal.

3

Design of Equipment

1.12 In general, all electrical equipment should be constructed of durable, flame-retardant, non-hygroscopic materials which are not subject to deterioration in the atmospheres and at the temperatures to which they are likely to be exposed. Where hygroscopic materials are used in contact with live parts, secondary non-hygroscopic insulation should be incorporated unless ingress of moisture is prevented by adequate sealing. Particular care should be taken to avoid corrosion due to contact between metals of dissimilar electrolytic potential.

> NOTE: Special consideration should be given to materials for items associated with systems which would be required to operate as long as possible in a fire, e.g. cables for certain alarms and shutdown systems, navigation lights, communication systems, emergency lighting, etc.

1.13 Insulating materials and insulated windings should be resistant to moisture, sea-air and oil vapour, unless special precautions are taken to protect them from the deleterious effects of such environments.

1.14 Where liquid coolants are used, consideration should be given to the detection of liquids in an equipment enclosure and provision of an alarm indication. In addition, for semiconductor converters, flow of coolant should be monitored to operate an alarm in the event of significant reduction of flow.

> NOTE: Attention is drawn to the need to guard against the leakage of coolant into the cooling liquid, e.g. where liquid to liquid heat exchangers are fitted.

1.15 The distances between live parts of different potential and between live parts and the case or other earthed metal, whether across surfaces or in air, should be adequate for the working and transient voltage having regard to the nature of the insulating material and arcing under operating and fault conditions.

1.16 The design of equipment should provide accessibility to all parts requiring inspection or replacement in service.

1.17 Enclosure

(1) Enclosing cases for electrical equipment, junction boxes, joint boxes, etc., should be of adequate mechanical strength and rigidity to protect the contents and prevent distortion under all likely conditions of service.

(2) Depending on its location, equipment should normally have the degree of protection as given in Table 1.1 as a minimum. Where the protection is not achieved by the equipment itself, other means or the location where it is installed should achieve the degree of protection required in the Table, unless access is limited to authorised persons, when additional precautions may be necessary.

NOTE: The designations to indicate the degree of protection in Table 1.1, consisting of the characteristic letters IP followed by two numerals, are in accordance with the classification given in BS 5490.

1.18 Apparatus should be provided with suitable cable glands, bushings or conduit entries. All entries should maintain the degree of protection provided by the enclosure of the associated apparatus.

1.19 The means of fixing current-carrying parts should be independent of the means of making connection thereto.

1.20 Apparatus should be provided with suitable terminals, clearly marked, placed in an accessible position convenient for external connections. The terminals should be effectively secured and should be so spaced and / or shielded as to minimise the risk of accidental earthing or short-circuiting. Adequate clearance should be allowed between the cable entries and terminals so that cables can be drawn in and connected without damage.
Enclosures containing delicate apparatus should be provided with means to allow easy termination of cables without exposing such apparatus to the possibility of damage.

1.21 Enclosures of fixed apparatus which are liable to exceed a temperature of 80°C should be so located or guarded as to prevent persons coming accidentally into contact with such equipment.

Installation. Location and Protection of Equipment

1.22 Construction and location

Compartments in which electrical apparatus is placed should be suitably constructed and ventilated to deal with the waste heat liberated by the apparatus under full load conditions at the appropriate cooling water or ambient air temperatures.

1.23 Electrical equipment should, as far as practicable, be so placed that it is not exposed to risk of mechanical damage or excessive vibration. If equipment must be installed in locations subject to vibration, e.g. steering compartments, consideration should be given to mounting it on anti-vibration mountings and metal enclosures provided with flexible arrangements for earthing.

1.24 Electrical equipment should be so selected and located or protected that the effects of exposure to sea-air, water, steam, oil or oil fumes, spray, ice formation, etc., is minimised. It should be located well clear of boilers, steam, oil or water pipes, and engine exhaust pipes or manifolds, unless specifically designed for such locations. If pipes must be run adjacent to electrical equipment there should be no joints in the immediate vicinity of the equipment.

5

NOTE: Where sprinkler heads or water spraying devices are fitted for fire-fighting, consideration should be given to the siting of electrical equipment which would be seriously affected by the inadvertent operation of the extinguishing arrangement. This is particularly applicable to switchgear and switch rooms, where a suitable alternative method of extinguishing should be used.

1.25 Horizontal rotating machines should, where practicable, be installed fore-and-aft to minimise the effects of rolling. Where a machine is installed athwartships or vertically, the design of bearings and the arrangement for their lubrication should be adequate to withstand the rolling encountered in heavy weather and operation for prolonged periods at the list specified in 1.11 of these Recommendations.

1.26 All electrical equipment should be so enclosed or guarded as may be necessary to prevent danger so that live parts cannot inadvertently be touched.

1.27 Where an item of equipment or enclosure contains live parts that are not capable of being isolated by a single device, a warning notice should be placed in such a position that any person gaining access to live parts will be warned of the need to use the appropriate isolating devices, unless an interlocking arrangement is provided so that all the circuits concerned are isolated.

1.28 Electrical apparatus should be so installed that sufficient space is available for inspection and maintenance.

1.29 In every ship in which electric power is used for essential services the generators, switchgear, motors and associated control gear for such services should be so situated or protected that they will continue to operate satisfactorily in the event of partial flooding by bilge water above the tank top in the space in which they are situated. The design criterion for "partial flooding" should be assumed to be a depth of water 1/12th beam but not exceeding a depth of 1.5 m. Where this recommendation is impracticable for horizontally mounted propulsion motors, the minimum requirement is watertight to underside of the motor shaft.

Electrical Equipment in Flammable and Explosive Dust Atmospheres

1.30 Because of the potential dangers introduced by electrical equipment and the difficulty in maintaining its safe characteristics in service, such equipment should not be installed where flammable gases / vapours or explosive dusts are liable to accumulate except where it is essential and it is specifically provided for by these Recommendations.

1.31 Where risk of explosion from flammable gases / vapours could arise, equipment should be of a safe type, certified for the gases / vapours involved

6

and should comply with BS 229, BS 4683, BS 5501 or with an equivalent National or International Standard. Certified safe type equipment includes the following types of protection:

Intrinsically safe	— EEx 'i' / Ex 'i';
Increased safety	— EEx 'e' / Ex 'e';
Flameproof	— EEx 'd' / Ex 'd';
Pressurized enclosure	— EEx 'p' / Ex 'p'.

1.32 Where risk of explosion from combustible dusts could arise, equipment should comply with BS 6467 or with an equivalent National or International Standard.

1.33 Section 14 gives details of electrical equipment permitted in battery compartments.

1.34 Section 16 gives details of the requirements for trace heating systems.

1.35 Section 23 gives details of electrical equipment permitted onboard tankers intended for the carriage in bulk of oil cargoes and other types of ships where oil or liquids of similar hazards are processed, handled or stored.

1.36 Statutory requirements as listed in Part 2,1.1 and 1.7, govern the electrical equipment permitted onboard the following types of ships:

ships carrying dangerous chemicals in bulk;
ships carrying liquified gases in bulk;
ships carrying dangerous goods and materials hazardous only in bulk;
ships with spaces for carrying vehicles with fuel in their tanks for their own propulsion.

1.37 Electrical equipment for use in stores containing paint or other flammable fluids should be of a certified safe type except that Ex 'e' motors are not permitted. All switches and protective devices should interrupt all poles or phases and should be located in a non-hazardous area. Such switches and protective devices should be suitably labelled for identification purposes.

1.38 Electrical equipment for use in other spaces / areas where flammable gases / vapours and / or explosive dusts are liable to accumulate or where explosive materials are handled or stored, is to be of a type acceptable to the Appropriate Authority.

NOTE 1 BS 5345 gives guidance on the installation and maintenance of electrical equipment for use in potentially explosive atmospheres.

NOTE 2 Special precautions may be necessary where risk of explosion from combustible dusts and flammable gases / vapours could arise simultaneously.

1.39 For cables within hazardous areas, see 11.17(2).

Table 1.1 Minimum requirements for degree of protection (BS 5490)

(1) Example of location	(2) Condition in location	(3) Design according to degree of protection	(4) Equipment — X means complies with column (3). — means not recommended.							
			Switchboards, Control gear Motor starters	Generators	Motors	Transformers Semiconductor convertors	Luminaires	Heating appliances	Cooking appliances	Accessories (e.g. switches, branches boxes)
Dry accommodation spaces	Danger of touching live parts only	IP20	X	—	X	X	X	X	X	X
Dry control rooms			X	—	X	X	X	X	X	X
Control rooms (navigation bridge)		IP22	X	—	X	X	X	X	X	X
Engine and boiler rooms above floor	Danger of dripping liquid and / or moderate mechanical damage		X	X	X	X	X	X	X	IP44
Steering gear rooms			X	X	X	X	X	X	—	IP44
Refrigerating machinery rooms (excluding ammonia plants)			X	—	X	X	X	X	—	IP44
Emergency machinery rooms			X	X	X	X	X	X	—	IP44
General store rooms			X	—	X	X	X	X	—	X
Pantries			X	—	X	X	X	X	X	IP44
Provision rooms			X	—	X	X	X	X	—	X
Bathrooms and showers	Increased danger of liquid and / or mechanical damage	IP34	—	—	—	—	X	IP44	—	IP55
Engine and boiler rooms below floor			—	—	IP44	—	X	IP44	—	IP55
Closed fuel oil separator rooms			IP44	—	IP44	—	X	IP44	—	IP55
Closed lubricating oil separator rooms			IP44	—	IP44	—	X	IP44	—	IP55
Ballast pump rooms	Increased danger of liquid and mechanical damage	IP44	X	—	X	X	IP34	X	—	IP55
Refrigerated rooms			—	—	X	—	IP34	X	—	IP55
Galleys and laundries			X	—	X	X	IP34	X	X	X
Shaft or pipe tunnels in double bottom	Danger of liquid spraying	IP55	X	—	X	X	X	X	—	IP56
Holds for general cargo	Presence of cargo dust Serious mechanical damage Aggressive fumes	IP55	—	—	—	—	X	—	—	X
Open decks	Danger of liquid in massive quantities	IP56	X	—	X	—	IP55	X	—	X

NOTE 1 Certified safe-type equipment may need additional enclosure requirements for spaces on open decks or other spaces where wet conditions are expected. The examples above may be used as guidelines.

NOTE 2 Socket-outlets should not be installed in spaces that require certified safe-type equipment.

SECTION 2

EARTHING OF NON-CURRENT-CARRYING PARTS

2.1   Unless specifically exempted by the following exemptions (i to x), all exposed metal of the electrical installation, other than current-carrying parts, should be earthed.

Exemptions:

(i)   Lamp-caps, where suitably shrouded.

(ii)   Shades, reflectors and guards supported on lampholders or luminaires constructed of, or shrouded in, non-conducting material.

(iii)   Metal parts on, or screws in or through, non-conducting materials, which are separated by such material from current-carrying parts and from earthed non-current-carrying parts in such a way that in normal use they cannot become live or come into contact with earthed parts.

(iv)   Portable appliances having double insulation (or, in certain circumstances, reinforced insulation) in accordance with a British Standard which has been approved for the purpose.

NOTE: For further information see BS 2754 and Appendix B.

(v)   Bearing housings which are insulated in order to prevent circulation of current in the bearings.

(vi)   Clips for fluorescent lamps.

(vii)   Cable clips.

(viii)   Apparatus supplied at extra-low voltage.

(ix)   Apparatus of 'all-insulated' construction in which the insulation enclosing the apparatus is durable and substantially continuous.

(x)   Fixed apparatus or parts of apparatus which although not shrouded in insulating material is nevertheless otherwise so guarded that it cannot be touched and cannot come in contact with exposed metal.

2.2   Non-current-carrying parts not exempted in 2.1 should be earthed by one or more of the means described in 2.2(1) to 2.2(5).

(1)   Metal frames or enclosures of apparatus should be connected to the hull of metal ships in a manner to ensure a common potential. See 2.6 for ships with non-metallic hulls.

A cable metallic sheath, armour or braid should not be solely relied upon for earthing purposes if:

(i)   the apparatus is not in continuous contact with the hull of metal ships e.g. steel enclosure on an insulated support;

9

(ii)   the apparatus operates at a voltage above 1 kV;
(iii) the earth loop impedance calculated using the metallic armour or braid is not low enough to permit the passage of a current at least three times the fuse rating for fuse protected circuits or 1.5 times the tripping current of any excess current circuit breaker used to protect the circuit.

NOTE 1   For all of the above it will be necessary to provide additional earthing connections which should generally comply with 2.3. These earthing connections should be from the relevant enclosure to the cable metallic sheath and / or to the hull of metal ships. In 2.2(1)(i) and (ii) the earthing connection could be to local steelwork if this was connected to the hull of metal ships. In (iii) it would be necessary to increase the size of the cable or provide an earth cable in parallel with the cable armour. For (ii) bonding of the enclosure to the metallic cable armour and to the hull of metal ships would be necessary.

NOTE 2   For multiple cable connections, in order to ensure earth fault current values stated in 2.2(1) (iii) the calculated earth loop impedance should be increased by a factor of 1.25 to allow for unequal current sharing by the metallic armour or braid of the various cables.

NOTE 3   When earth leakage relays or circuit breakers are provided a higher earth loop impedance than required by 2.2(1)(iii) may be acceptable.

NOTE 4   A correction multiplier of 0.5 should be applied to the maximum permitted impedance values in all cases where it is anticipated that the environmental conditions could lead to accelerated degradation of earth loop paths.

NOTE 5   Fortuitous paths such as metallic cable armouring in contact with the hull of metal ships or with cable clips (other than those clips specifically applied for earthing purposes), etc., should not be taken into consideration when assessing the current that will flow under fault conditions.

(2)   The metallic sheaths, armour or braid of cables should be effectively earthed to the hull of metal ships at both ends, with the exception of the following:

(i)   Single point earthing may be applied to single core cables for a.c. systems.
(ii)   In final sub-circuits, earthing may be at the supply end only.
(iii) Single point earthing may also be applied to cables for control and instrumentation, control circuits and intrinsically safe systems, etc., where this is required for technical or security reasons. See also Appendix D.

It should be ensured that all metallic sheaths, armour and braid are made electrically continuous throughout their length. All earthing should be effected by means of clamps, crimped or soldered joints or, alternatively, by glands, specially designed for the purpose, which are firmly attached to, and in effective electrical contact with, a metal enclosure or structure earthed in accordance with these Recommendations.

(3)   Metallic conduit may be earthed by being screwed into a metal enclosure, or by nuts on both sides of the wall of a metal enclosure, provided that surfaces in contact are clean and free from rust, scale or paint, and that the enclosure is earthed in accordance with these Recommendations. The connection should be painted immediately after assembly in order to inhibit corrosion.

> NOTE: Where metallic conduit is used for earthing purposes it should be screwed into the associated enclosures.

(4)   Alternatively to the methods described in 2.2(2) and 2.2(3), metallic cable sheaths and armour, and conduit, may be earthed by means of clamps or clips of corrosion-resistant metal making effective contact with the metallic sheath or armour and earthed metal.

(5)   All joints in metal conduits and ducts and in metal sheaths of cables which are used for earth-continuity should be soundly made and protected, where necessary, against corrosion.

2.3   Earthing connections

(1)   Every earthing conductor should be of copper or other corrosion-resistant material and should be securely installed and protected where necessary against damage and also, where necessary, against electrolytic corrosion. Connections should be so secured that they cannot work loose under vibration.

(2)   The nominal cross-sectional area of every copper earthing conductor should be not less than is required in Table 2.1 or Table 2.2, as appropriate. Every other earthing conductor should have a conductance not less than that specified for a copper earthing conductor.

(3)   Metal parts of portable appliances, other than current-carrying parts and parts exempted in 2.1, should be earthed by means of an earth-continuity conductor in the flexible cable or cord which complies with Table 2.1 and is earthed, e.g. through the associated plug and socket-outlet.

2.4   Every connection to the hull of metal ships should be made in an accessible position, and should be secured by a screw or stud of diameter not less than 6 mm which should be used for this purpose only. In all circumstances care should be taken to ensure bright metallic surfaces at the contact areas immediately before the nut or screw is tightened and, where necessary, to protect the joint against electrolytic corrosion.

2.5   Attention is drawn to the earthing requirements covered by 7.13(2), 22.5 and D.4(6).

2.6   Additional requirements for ships with non-metallic hulls

(1)   A main earth conductor bar should be provided at a suitable location, for example, at the main switchboard, to which all non-current-carrying parts not exempted under 2.1 should be connected.

(2)   The main earth conductor bar should be connected to the main earthing plate described in 2.6(3) by a copper conductor having a minimum cross-sectional area of 64 mm^2 preferably of solid strip construction.

(3)   A main earthing plate for communications, lightning and personnel protection should be provided. It should be of not less than 0.25 m^2 in area installed below the light-load waterline so as to remain immersed under all conditions of heel. The earthing plate should be of unpainted copper or other conducting material compatible with sea water. Two pillars should be provided, one for connection to the main earth conductor bar and one to the lightning down conductor described in 22.4, made of the same material as the earthing plate and solidly connected to it by welded joints. The establishment of electrochemical corrosion cells with other immersed metallic fittings should be avoided.

(4)   To minimise electromagnetic interference, earthing connections should be run with the associated power cables wherever practical. Three core cable is preferred for lighting circuits.

(5)   Earthing connections of equipment which are sensitive to electromagnetic interference should be made directly to the main earth conductor bar or the main earthing plate.

(6)   The earthing system in accordance with this Section and the lightning protective system in accordance with Section 22 should be run separately down to the pillars at the main earthing plate.

(7)   To dissipate possible charge build up in ships with non-metallic hulls constructed of high resistivity (surface and volume resistivities greater than 10^8 ohms and 10^6 ohms per metre (respectively) it is recommended that all metallic objects over 0.6 m in length and over 0.4 m^2 in surface area are earthed.

> NOTE: It may be desirable to bond to the main earth system all metal parts which are in direct contact with the sea, in order to minimise the effects of electrolytic corrosion.

Table 2.1 Size of earth-continuity conductors and earthing connections*

Type of earthing connection	Cross-sectional area of associated current-carrying conductor	Minimum cross-sectional area of copper earthing connection
(1) Earth-continuity conductor in flexible cable or flexible cord	Any	Same as current-carrying conductor up to 16 mm^2 and half above 16 mm^2 but at least 16mm^2
(2) Earth-continuity conductor incorporated in a fixed cable*	Any	For cables having an insulated earth-continuity conductor: (i) a cross-section equal to the main conductors for up to and including 16 mm^2 but minimum 1.5 mm^2 (ii) a cross-section not less than 50 per cent of the cross-section of the main conductor when the latter is more than 16mm^2 but at least 16mm^2
(3) Separate fixed conductor	(i) not exceeding 3 mm^2	Same as current-carrying conductor subject to 1.5 mm^2 for stranded earthing connection, or 3 mm^2 for unstranded earthing connection
	(ii) Exceeding 3 mm^2 but not exceeding 125 mm^2	One-half the cross-sectional area of the current-carrying conductor, subject to a minimum of 3 mm^2
	(iii) Exceeding 125 mm^2	64 mm^2

* Except for a flat-twin-and-earth PVC insulated cable to BS 6004. See Table 2.2.

Table 2.2   Size of earth-continuity conductor in flat-twin-and-earth PVC insulated PVC sheathed cables to BS 6004

Size of current-carrying conductor		Size of wires forming earth-continuity conductor	
Nominal cross-sectional area	No. and diameter (mm) of wires	Approximate cross-sectional area	No. and diameter (mm) of wires
1	2	3	4
mm^2		mm^2	
1.0	1/1.13	1.0	1/1.13
1.5	1/1.38	1.0	1/1.13
2.5	1/1.78	1.5	1/1.38
4	7/0.85	1.5	1/1.38
6	7/1.04	2.5	1/1.78
10	7/1.35	4	7/0.85
16	7/1.70	6	7/1.04

SECTION 3

APPLICATION OF DIVERSITY FACTORS

3.1   The cables of final sub-circuits should be rated in accordance with the total connected load.

3.2   Circuits supplying two or more final sub-circuits should be rated in accordance with the total connected load, subject where justifiable, to the application of a diversity factor in accordance with 3.3 and 3.4.

3.3   Conductors and switchgear

(1)   A diversity factor may be applied to the calculation of the cross-sectional area of conductors and to the rating of switchgear provided that the known or anticipated conditions in a particular part of the installation are suitable for the application of diversity.

(2)   Where spare ways are provided on a distribution board an allowance for future increase in load should be added to the total connected load before any diversity factor is applied.

3.4   The diversity factor for power circuits should take account of the known or anticipated conditions. The calculations should be based on the full load ratings of motors and the characteristics of the generators.

3.5   The diversity factor applied, where justifiable, to the loading calculation of cables, switchgear and generators supplying groups of winch motors or crane motors should be based upon the estimated duty cycle of the motors in the group, taking into account the frequency and duration of motor starting loads.

3.6   Assessment curves

For series resistance controlled d.c. motors assessment curves in Figure 3.1 have been found to be satisfactory.
    For variable voltage / current controlled equipment such as Ward Leonard or thyristor apparatus operating on d.c. or a.c. systems assessment curves in Figure 3.2 have been found to be satisfactory.
    For a.c. cage induction motors assessment curves in Figure 3.3 have been found to be satisfactory if the associated a.c. generators comply with 1.4(1) and 9.19.
    In each case, curve 'a' represents the factor to be applied for assessing generators and curve 'b' applies to cables and switchgear.
    All the assessment curves are based on motors of equal rating; if they are of different values suitable computations would be necessary. All the diversity

15

factors should be taken as a minimum and cables, switchgear and generators supplying winch motors and crane motors should be capable of carrying continuously (subject to voltage drop), the currents calculated by applying a diversity factor to the total connected load of winch motors and / or crane motors

Where the cables feeding winch motors and / or crane motors supply in addition other equipment, the current upon which the cross-sectional area of the conductors of the cables is based should allow for the coincidence of the various loads.

NOTE: The term "full load" applies to the full load kW (or current) or full load kVA input of the winch or crane motor at its maximum shaft output rating.

3.7   Refrigerated containers

A diversity factor may be applied for refrigerated containers when deciding the capacity of generators and distribution transformers. The final decision can only be reached by consideration of the type of container, the cargo mix between chilled and frozen and the ratio of hot to pre-cooled containers for the applicable trade.

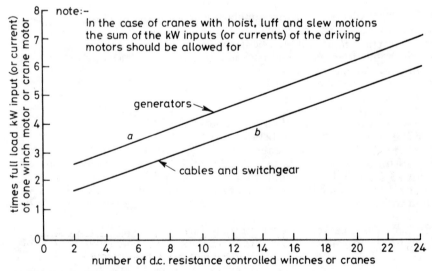

Figure 3.1   DC systems

16

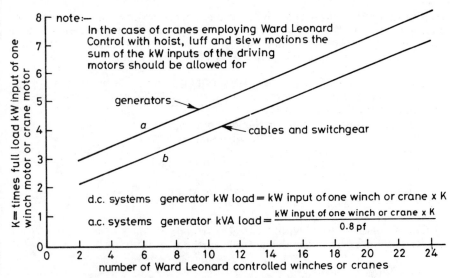

Figure 3.2   Ward Leonard control for dc and ac systems

The following text appears within the figure:

note:—
In the case of cranes employing Ward Leonard Control with hoist, luff and slew motions the sum of the kW inputs of the driving motors should be allowed for

generators
a
cables and switchgear
b

d.c. systems   generator kW load = kW input of one winch or crane x K

a.c. systems   generator kVA load = $\dfrac{\text{kW input of one winch or crane x K}}{0.8\,\text{pf}}$

(y-axis) K= times full load kW input of one winch motor or crane motor

(x-axis) number of Ward Leonard controlled winches or cranes

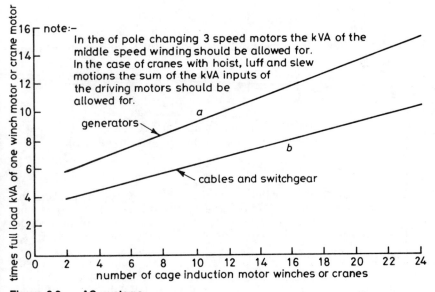

Figure 3.3   AC systems

The following text appears within the figure:

note:—
In the of pole changing 3 speed motors the kVA of the middle speed winding should be allowed for.
In the case of cranes with hoist, luff and slew motions the sum of the kVA inputs of the driving motors should be allowed for.

generators
a
cables and switchgear
b

(y-axis) times full load kVA of one winch motor or crane motor

(x-axis) number of cage induction motor winches or cranes

17

SECTION 4

AC SYSTEMS

(Where a.c. values are quoted in the Recommendations these are r.m.s. unless otherwise stated)

4.1   Generation

The following systems are recognised as standard for a.c. generation:

   (i)   3-phase 3-wire insulated;
  (ii) 3-phase 3-wire with neutral earthed;
 (iii) 3-phase 4-wire with neutral earthed.

4.2   Primary distribution

The following systems are recognised as standard for primary distribution:

   (i)   3-phase 3-wire insulated;
  (ii) 3-phase 3-wire with neutral earthed;
 (iii) 3-phase 4-wire with neutral earthed;
 (iv) single-phase 2-wire insulated.

4.3   Secondary distribution

The following systems are recognised as standard for secondary distribution:

   (i)   3-phase 3-wire insulated;
  (ii) 3-phase 3-wire with neutral earthed;
 (iii) 3-phase 4-wire with neutral earthed;
 (iv) single-phase 2-wire insulated;
  (v) single-phase 2-wire with one pole earthed;
 (vi) single-phase 2-wire with mid-point of system earthed.

4.4   Hull return systems

The hull return system of distribution should not be used for any purpose in a tanker, or for power, heating or lighting in any other ship of 1600 tonnes gross tonnage and upwards. This requirement does not preclude under conditions approved by the Appropriate Authority the use of:

   (i) limited and locally earthed systems; or
  (ii) insulation level monitoring devices provided the circulating current does not exceed 30 mA under the most unfavourable conditions.

18

Table 4.1 Voltages for a.c. appliances

Applications 1	Recognised standard voltages 2	Maximum voltages 3
(1) Heating and cooking equipment securely fixed and permanently connected	3-phase 115 415 240 440 380 Single- 115 415 phase 220 440 240	3-phase 500 Single- 500 phase
(2) Fixed lighting	Single- 115 240 phase 220	Single- 254 phase
(3) Socket-outlets for hand-held tools and lamps. See B.2		
(i) Where a safety isolating transformer is used supplying only one socket outlet	Single- 50 220 phase 115 240	Single- 254 phase
(ii) Supplied without the restrictions in (i) above	(a)Single- 24 50 phase 48 (b)Single- 115 with phase midpoint earthed	Single- 50 phase Single- 60 phase to earth
(4) Supply to equipment other than in (3) above, in dry areas of accommodation such as public rooms, cabins and alleyways, for general purposes, connected by flexible cable through a socket-outlet or direct	Single- 115 phase 220 240	Single- 254 phase
(5) Socket-outlets other than in (3) and (4) above. See B.4	115 415 220 440 240	3-phase 500
(6) Internal communications	Single- 12 220 phase 24 240 115	Single- 254 phase
(7) Supplies to lifeboats or similar craft	Single- 12 phase 24 48	Single- 55 phase

4.5 Frequencies

The following frequencies are recognised as standard:

(i) 50 Hz;
(ii) 60 Hz.

4.6 Voltages

(1) Systems having a nominal voltage in excess of 15 kV should be the subject of special consideration and should be to the satisfaction of the Appropriate Authority.

(2) Nominal system voltages for appliances detailed in column 1 of Table 4.1 should not exceed the values given in column 3.

NOTE: A system operating at over 1 kV should be considered when the use of a lower voltage would result in:

(i) a prospective short-circuit current which could occur at any point in the system in service exceeding approximately 70 kA symmetrical; or
(ii) the current rating of any generator exceeding approximately 4 kA.

SECTION 5

DC SYSTEMS

5.1   The following systems are recognized as standard; where other systems are used additional precautions may be necessary:

(i)   2-wire insulated;
(ii) 2-wire with one pole earthed, but without hull return;
(iii) 3-wire with middle wire earthed but without hull return.

5.2   The nominal voltage of supply should not exceed the values given in column 3 of Table 5.1.

5.3   Hull return systems

The hull return system of distribution should not be used for any purpose in a tanker, or for power, heating or lighting in any other ship of 1600 tonnes gross tonnage and upwards. This requirement does not preclude under conditions approved by the Appropriate Authority the use of:

(i)   impressed current cathodic protective systems;
(ii) limited and locally earthed systems; or
(iii) insulation level monitoring devices provided the circulating current does not exceed 30 mA under the most unfavourable conditions.

Table 5.1   Voltages for d.c. systems

Application 1	Recognised standard voltages 2	Maximum voltages 3
Power	110, 220, 600, 750	—
Cooking and heating	110, 220	250
Lighting and socket-outlets	24, 110, 220	250
Internal communications	6, 12, 24, 48, 110, 220	250
Supplies to lifeboats or similar craft	12, 24, 48	55

SECTION 6

SWITCHGEAR, SWITCHBOARDS AND DISTRIBUTION BOARDS

General

6.1   Position and arrangement of switchboards

(1)   The busbars of the main switchboard should be subdivided where the total installed capacity of the main generators exceeds 3 MW. The subdivision may be effected by removable links, circuit-breakers or other suitable means so that the main generators and any supplies to duplicated services which are directly connected to the busbars are, so far as practicable, equally divided between the sections.

> NOTE: The advantages of such an arrangement should also be taken into consideration in the design of switchboards where the installed electrical power of the main generators is less than 3 MW.

(2)   Every main and emergency switchboard should be provided with non-conducting handrails, fitted front and rear.

(3)   Platforms at front and rear of switchboards should have non-slip surfaces. Where access to live parts within switchboards is normally possible the surfaces should, in addition, be insulated.

(4)   An unobstructed passage-way not less than 1 m wide should be provided in front of the switchboard. When the switchboard contains withdrawable equipment, e.g. circuit-breaker and starter chassis, the unobstructed passage-way should not be less than 0.4 m wide with this equipment in its fully withdrawn position.

(5)   Any access at the rear of a switchboard should be ample to permit maintenance and, in general not less than 0.6 m in the clear, except the width may be reduced to 0.5 m in way of stiffeners and frames. Passage-ways behind switchboards should be of ample height and should, where the switchboard rear is open, be provided at each end with an access door fitted with an external lock which can, at all times, be opened from the passage-way. Such access doors should bear a prominent and permanent indication of the maximum voltage.

6.2   Construction of switchboards

(1)   Switchboards should comply with BS 5486 and be of substantial and

22

durable construction and should be capable of withstanding electromechanical stresses which may arise from short-circuits.

(2)   For voltages between poles, or to earth, exceeding 250 volts d.c. or 55 volts a.c., switchboards should be of the dead front or metal-enclosed type.

(3)   Every fuse mounted behind a switchboard should be easily accessible and should be well clear of busbars (excepting those mounted thereon for "back up" protection purposes), connections, circuit-breakers and exposed live parts. Fuses mounted on busbars should be shrouded to prevent inadvertent physical contact with the busbars.

6.3   Insulating materials

(1)   Insulating materials used in the construction of switchboards should be mechanically strong, flame-retardant and moisture-resistant. The surface finish should preferably be anti-tracking.

(2)   Parts of insulation which have been exposed by drilling or other machining operations should be coated with insulating varnish or enamel when necessary to retain the original insulating qualities.

(3)   Where semi-insulating materials, such as manufactured panel board, are used, all conducting parts on each insulated pole should be insulated from the panel with bushes and washers of mica or other flame-retardant and moisture-resistant insulating material.

6.4   Cables for internal wiring should be constructed in accordance with one of the following standards: BS 6141, BS 6195, BS 6231, or BS 6883.

6.5   Busbars should be of copper or aluminium and should comply with the appropriate requirements of BS 159. All joints should be made so as to inhibit corrosion. All such connections should be arranged and supported to withstand the mechanical forces which would be encountered during a short circuit.

6.6   Labels and identification

(1)   All switchboard instruments, controls and all principle items of equipment, both on external panels and inside the switchboard, should be provided with durable labels of flame-retardant material bearing clear and indelible indications. See also 27.7.

(2)   Circuit references should be provided for individual circuits.

(3)   Where a scheme of marking is used to identify switchboard busbars and / or connections to individual poles or phases the marking should be consistent throughout.

6.7   Rating of equalisers

(1)   The current rating of equaliser connections and equaliser switches, should be not less than half the rate full load current of the generator.

(2)   The current rating of equaliser busbars should be not less than half the rated full load current of the largest generator in the group.

6.8   Switchgear and fusegear

(1)   Circuit-breakers should comply with the requirements of BS 4752, Part 1.

(2)   Where other means of isolation are not available, all circuit-breakers and contactors forming part of the main switchboard should be provided with safe means of isolation for maintenance purposes, switches and isolators being constructed such that, as far as is practicable, moving parts may be adjusted or replaced without danger.

(3)   Every fuse should be provided with a suitable non-combustible insulating fuse carrier of such form as to protect a person handling it from shock and burns, except where suitable insulated detachable handles or other suitable devices are provided or the arrangements are such that, in distribution boards, a switch connected on the live side of the fuse is fitted thereto and a lid or door is provided to guard the fuse against unauthorised access. See also 8.13.

(4)   Effectual provision should be made for retaining in position all fuses subject to vibration or shock.

6.9   Measuring instruments

(1)   Switchboard instruments should comply with the requirements of BS 89 or BS 90, whichever is applicable. Instrument transformers should comply with the requirements of BS 3938 or BS 3941.

(2)   DC generators and systems

    (i)   For d.c. generators not operated in parallel, one voltmeter and one ammeter should be provided for each generator.

    (ii)   For parallel operation, at least one ammeter should be provided for each d.c. generator and one busbar voltmeter, together with either one voltmeter for each generator or one voltmeter with change-over switch for measuring each generator voltage.

    (iii)   The upper limit of the scale of every voltmeter should be approximately 120% of the normal voltage of the circuit and the scale should be provided with a red line to indicate normal voltage.
         The upper limit of the scale of every ammeter and wattmeter should be not less than 130% of the normal rating of the circuit in which it is installed. The scale should be provided with a red line indicating the normal full load.

24

(iv) Ammeters for use with generators which may operate in parallel should be capable of indicating reverse current up to 15% of the rated full load current of the generator.

(v) For 2-wire generators fitted with equaliser connections, the ammeter should be connected in the positive pole (i.e. the pole opposite to that connected to the series winding of the generator).

(vi) For 3-wire generators fitted with equaliser connections the ammeters should be connected between the equaliser connection and the armature.

(vii) For 3-wire systems supplied by a 3-wire generator, or by a balancer, an ammeter should be connected in each outer pole and a voltmeter between each pole of the busbars and the middle wire.

(3)   3-phase a.c. generators and systems

(i) For a.c. generators not operated in parallel, each generator should be provided with at least a voltmeter and a frequency meter, and an ammeter in each phase conductor or one ammeter and a selector switch designed to permit the reading of the current in each phase.

(ii) For a.c. generators operated in parallel, each generator should be provided with at least a wattmeter and an ammeter in each phase conductor or an ammeter and a selector switch designed to permit the reading of the current in each phase. For paralleling purposes, two voltmeters, two frequency meters and a synchronising system, the last named being controlled by a switch or plug and comprising a synchroscope and synchronising lamps. A plug or linked double-pole multi-way switch should be provided to enable one voltmeter and frequency meter to be connected to one phase of any one generator before the machine is connected to the busbars; the other voltmeter and frequency meter should be permanently connected to one phase of the busbars. The connection should be made to the corresponding phase of each generator.

(iii) The upper limit of the scale of every voltmeter should be approximately 120% of the normal voltage of the circuit and the scale should be provided with a red line to indicate normal voltage.
    The upper limit of the scale of every ammeter and wattmeter should be not less than 130% of the normal rating of the circuit in which it is installed. The scale should be provided with a red line indicating the normal full load.

(iv) Wattmeters for use with generators which may operate in parallel should be capable of indicating reverse power up to 15% of the rated full load of the generator.

6.10   Secondary windings of all current transformers for instruments, such as meters and protection relays, should be effectively earthed.

6.11   Earth indication

(1)   Every insulated distribution system, whether primary or secondary, should be provided with means to continuously indicate the state of insulation

from earth, arranged to give audible or visual warning of abnormally low levels of insulation.

(2)   Every earth indicating device should be so designed that the flow of current to earth through it is as low as practicable, but in no case should exceed 30 mA.

(3)   Where an earth-indicating system using either two or three lamps, as appropriate, is adopted, earth-indicating lamps should be of the metal filament type. The system employing a single lamp should not be used. To facilitate comparison of the brilliance of earth-indicating lamps they should be of clear glass and should be placed not more than 150 mm apart.

6.12   DC generator switchgear

For each d.c. generator installed, the following switchgear should be provided:

(1)   For generators not arranged to run in parallel: for a two-wire insulated system, either a double-pole circuit-breaker or a fuse in each pole and a double-pole linked switch. For ratings below 50 kW, see 8.5(1).

(2)   For generators arranged to run in parallel:

(i)   For two-wire insulated systems, a double-pole circuit-breaker.
(ii)   For two-wire compound-wound generators, an equaliser switch which should be so interlocked with each circuit-breaker that it must be closed before the circuit-breaker and cannot be opened until the main circuit is opened.
(iii) For two-wire systems the reverse-current protection should be connected on the positive pole (i.e. the pole opposite to that on which the equaliser connection is made).
(iv)   Circuit-breakers for turbine-driven generators should be suitable for operation in conjunction with the emergency overspeed trip, see 9.9.

See Section 8 for protection requirements.

6.13   Where three-phase a.c. generators are installed, there should be provided for each generator a triple-pole linked circuit-breaker. See Section 8 for protection requirements.

6.14   Solid earth connections.

(1)   In every distribution system which is designed to operate with an earth connection, no fuse, non-linked switch or non-linked circuit-breaker should be inserted in an earthed conductor.

(2)   The requirement of 6.14(1) should not preclude the provision (for testing purposes) of an isolating link having a current rating not less than that of the conductor which it serves to isolate. Such a link should be securely

26

fixed at its terminations by bolts or screws and should be used to isolate such a conductor only when the associated insulated poles or phases are isolated.

The use of neutral earthing switches for a.c. generators and transformers is permissible.

6.15   Automatic voltage regulators should be protected separately from all other instrument circuits. See also 8.9.

6.16   Control of outgoing circuits

(1)   Every outgoing circuit should be protected in each insulated pole or phase by a fuse or circuit-breaker. In addition, 2-wire circuits of rating exceeding 100 amperes protected by a fuse should be controlled, as a minimum, by a switch in one pole or phase.

(2)   Every 3-phase, 3-wire circuit should be controlled by a triple-pole linked circuit-breaker with an overload release in each insulated pole or alternatively by a fuse in each insulated pole and, for every circuit rated in excess of 60 amperes, by a triple-pole linked switch.

Special requirements for Distribution Boards

NOTE: 6.1 to 6.11, 6.14 and 6.16 apply where appropriate to distribution boards, except in so far as they are qualified by 6.17 and 6.18.

6.17   Enclosures

(1)   Distribution boards should be totally enclosed in metal cases or in robust non-combustible non-metallic cases.

(2)   In accommodation type areas, enclosures should be locked and accessible only to authorised persons. In such enclosures the board may be open pattern without further enclosure, but all live busbars, live parts and connections should be suitably shrouded with insulation so that live parts cannot be inadvertently touched. Any metalwork of such a board should be connected to earth.

6.18   The voltage of every distribution board should be indicated by a label bearing clear and indelible indication.

SECTION 7

DISTRIBUTION

7.1   If a cable is looped from board to board without passing through a protective device, the cable conductors should be of the same cross-section throughout.

7.2   Switches in conductors of insulated distribution systems should open all lines simultaneously.

7.3   Final sub-circuits

(1)   A final sub-circuit of rating exceeding 16 A should not supply more than one point, except as specifically permitted in 7.3(2) and 7.3(3). The number of points supplied by a final sub-circuit of rating not exceeding 16 A should in no case exceed:

    (i)   for 24 to   55 volt circuits — 10;
    (ii) for 110 to 115 volt circuits — 14;
   (iii) for 220 to 240 volt circuits — 18.

Exemption: In final sub-circuits of cornice lighting, panel lighting and electric signs, where lampholders are closely grouped, the number of lighting points supplied is unrestricted, provided that the maximum operating current in the sub-circuit does not exceed 10 A.

(2)   A final sub-circuit having a rating exceeding 16 A, but not exceeding 32 A, may supply two or more cooking appliances where these are installed in one space. In the absence of precise data the current demand should be assessed as the first 10 A of the total rated current of the connected cooking appliances, plus 30% of the remainder of the total rated current of the connected cooking appliances.

(3)   In dry areas of accommodation spaces, and in spaces having similar environmental conditions, ring final sub-circuits each protected by a 30 A or 32 A fuse or miniature circuit break may be installed to serve socket-outlets complying with BS 1363, provided that one pole of the supply is earthed. The maximum number of socket-outlets connected to each ring should be according to the estimated maximum demand of apparatus within the 30 A or 32 A rating, but should not exceed 18. The cables used for such ring final sub-circuits should have a minimum current carrying capacity of 20 A.

(4)   A separate final sub-circuit should be provided for every motor exceeding 0.5 kW output.

28

(5)   Lighting circuits should be supplied by final sub-circuits separate from those for heating and power requirements.

Exemption: 7.3(5) does not preclude the supply from a lighting circuit to a single fixed appliance taking a maximum of 2 A, such as a cabin fan, dry shaver, wardrobe heater or anti-condensation heaters for electronic and similar equipment.

(6)   The final sub-circuits of any hull return system of distribution should be two wire.

(7)   Every final sub-circuit should be separately connected to:
   (i)   a distribution board; or
   (ii) a switchboard.

7.4   If a ship is divided into fire zones, at least two separate circuits for lighting should be provided in each zone, one of which may be the circuit for the emergency lighting.

7.5   Any circuits terminating in a cargo space should be provided with multi-pole linked isolating switches outside that space and accessible only to authorised personnel. Provision should be made for the complete isolation and for the locking in the "off" position of the means of control of such circuits. This recommendation does not apply in respect of safety devices such as fire, smoke or gas detectors.

7.6   In main propelling-machinery spaces, in other large machinery spaces, in large galleys, and in corridors, stairways leading to boat decks and in public rooms, lamps should be supplied from at least two final sub-circuits, one of which may be the emergency circuit.
    Switches used to control emergency lighting should not be accessible to unauthorised persons.

7.7   Navigation lights

(1)   All ships and vessels of every type must comply with the International Regulations for Preventing Collisions at Sea 1972, as amended. Ships of every type and size are required to be provided with "steaming lights" which comprise masthead, side, stern, anchor, not-under-command and, if applicable, special purpose lights. The construction and installation of navigation lights should be to the satisfaction of the Appropriate Authority.

(2)   Ships should be provided with primary and alternative lanterns for each of the navigation lights required by the Collision Regulations, except that alternative lights are not required for ships less than 24.4 metres in length. Primary lanterns should be electric. Alternative lanterns should be electric except that oil lanterns may be used in ships (other than tankers) less than 20 metres in length (all lanterns) and less than 50 metres in length (all lanterns except masthead).

(3)   The arrangements described in 7.7(4) and 7.7(5) below apply to all passenger ships and to new cargo ships of 500 tons or over. For other ships and for further navigation light information reference should be made to "Survey of lights and signalling equipment. Instructions for the guidance of surveyors", see Part 2, 4.

(4)   Primary electric steaming lanterns with electric alternatives

  (i) Each light should be connected by a separate cable to a distribution board reserved for navigation lights, fitted in an accessible place and under control of the officer of the watch.
  (ii) There should be two essentially separate power supply systems to the distribution board — one from the main switchboard and one from the emergency switchboard.

NOTE: Where a transitional source of emergency power is required by SOLAS the arrangements should enable the lights to be supplied from this source in addition to the emergency generator.

  (iii) So far as is practicable, the arrangements should be such that a fire, fault or mechanical damage at any one point will not render both systems inoperative; it is accepted, however, that the systems must come together at some point where the changeover can be effected. This should preferably be at or near the distribution board.
  (iv) Each light should be controlled and protected in each insulated pole by a switch and fuse or by a circuit-breaker mounted in the distribution board.
  (v) Each light should be provided with an automatic indicator to give an audible and / or visual alarm in the event of lamp failure. If a visual signal is used, which is connected in series with the steaming light, means to prevent failure of the indicator extinguishing the steaming light should be provided. If an audible device alone is used it should be connected to an independent source of supply, e.g. a battery, and provision should be made for testing this supply.

NOTE 1   The indicator board may be combined with the steaming light distribution board.

NOTE 2   Light failure indicator / alarm systems are not required in vessels under 24.4 m in length.

  (vi) The use of junction boxes in navigation light circuits, other than those provided for connecting the lanterns to the fixed wiring of the electrical installation, should be avoided. Cables for different circuits should not use the same junction box.
  (vii) Where systems at reduced voltage (e.g. 24 V) are used, voltage drop in cables requires particular attention and should not exceed 6% of the nominal voltage.

(5)   Electric steaming lanterns with oil alternatives
The arrangements should be as described in 7.7(4) but may be relaxed in accordance with the following:

place of

(i) The requirements of 7.7(4)(ii) ~~may be replaced by the following requirement:~~
Provision should be made in the distribution board to change over the navigation lights to an alternative circuit.
~~(ii) The requirements of 7.7(4)(iii) need not apply.~~

7.8   Steering gear

(1)   Electric or electro-hydraulic steering gear should have two independent sets of supply cables which should be connected direct to the main switchboard, except that, where there is an emergency source of power, one set may be connected to the main switchboard via the emergency switchboard.
Each circuit should have adequate capacity for supplying all the motors which are normally connected to it and which operate simultaneously. If transfer arrangements are provided in the steering gear compartment, to permit either circuit to supply any motor or combination of motors, the capacity of each circuit should be adequate for the most severe load condition.
The two sets of cables should be separated throughout their length as widely as practicable.
An auxiliary electric or electro-hydraulic steering gear may be connected to one of the circuits supplying the main steering gear.

(2)   Protection of steering gear circuits should be in accordance with 8.6, 8.8(2), 8.8(5), 8.8(6) and 13.3.(1).

(3)   The motors driving steering gear power units should be arranged so that they are:

(i) Provided with running indicators in the bridge and the machinery control room or other position required by the Appropriate Authority;
(ii) Capable of being brought into operation from a position on the bridge;
(iii) Provided with an audible and visual alarm on the bridge that will operate in the event of a power failure to any steering gear power unit.

(4)   Every steering gear control system should be:

(i) Separately supplied by a steering gear power circuit located within the steering gear compartment or directly from a point on the switchboard adjacent to the busbars supplying that steering gear power unit;

(ii)   Provided with means in the steering gear compartment for disconnecting the control system from the steering gear it serves;

(iii) Capable of being brought into operation from a position on the bridge;

(iv)   Provided with an audible and visual alarm on the bridge that will operate in the event of a failure of the electric power supply to the control system.

(5)   Arrangements to transfer power supplies for the steering gear control system to another busbar may be fitted.

(6)   Where more than one electric steering gear control system is provided, the cables for each should be separated throughout their length as widely as practicable.

NOTE 1   An alternative power supply is required for the steering gear of ships above certain tonnage.

NOTE 2   Duplicated steering gear control systems are required for certain ships.

NOTE 3   For further information on the steering gear arrangements reference should be made to Merchant Shipping (Passenger Ship Construction and Survey) Regulations 1984 and the Merchant Shipping (Cargo Ship Construction and Survey) Regulations 1984, see Part 2, 1.1.

7.9   Submersible bilge pumps

(1)   Motors of permanently installed emergency submersible bilge pumps should be connected to the emergency switchboard, if any.

(2)   Cables and their connections to such pumps should be capable of operating under a head of water equal to their distance below the bulkhead deck. The cables should be armoured and should be installed in continuous lengths from above the bulkhead deck to the motor terminals and should enter the air bell from the bottom. Cables of other types having equivalent mechanical protection may be used as an alternative to the armoured cables.

(3)   Under all circumstances it should be possible to start the motor of a permanently installed submersible bilge pump from a convenient point above the bulkhead deck.

7.10   Arrangements for isolation of every heating and / or cooking appliance should be provided. See also 16.5.

7.11   Except for essential services, a pilot lamp installed as an integral part of an appliance or accessory need not be individually protected provided that the protection device of the main circuit is rated at not more than 16A. See also 8.9.

7.12   Emergency supplies

(1)   Where the emergency system is being supplied by a battery, an indicator should be mounted on or near a permanently manned main control or navigating position to show when the battery is being discharged.

(2)   Suitable switch gear should be provided at the emergency switchboard for isolating the main switchboard and all circuits other than emergency circuits.

> NOTE: Attention is drawn to the Merchant Shipping (Passenger Ship Construction and Survey) Regulations 1984 and the Merchant Shipping (Cargo Ship Construction and Survey) Regulations 1984, see Part 2, 1.1.

7.13   Shore supply

(1)   Where arrangements are made for the supply of electricity from an external source on shore or elsewhere, a suitable connection box, having terminals of ample size and suitable shape to facilitate satisfactory connection and convenient reception of the supply, should be installed in a position in the ship such as to minimise the length of the flexible cables from the external source.
    Permanently installed cables should be provided between the connection box and the main switchboard. See also 8.11.

(2)   An earth terminal should be provided for connection of the hull of the ship to the shore earth. For ships with non metallic hulls, facilities should be provided for the shore earth to be connected to the main earth conductor bar. See also 2.6.1.

(3)   An indicator should be provided at the main switchboard to show when the shore supply is energised.

(4)   Means should be provided for checking the polarity (for d.c.) or the phase sequence (for 3 phase a.c.) of the incoming supply in relation to the ship's system.

(5)   At the connection box a notice should be provided giving full information on the system supply and the rated voltage (and frequency, if a.c.) of the ship's system, and the procedure for carrying out the connection.

SECTION 8

PROTECTION

8.1　General

(1)　Protective devices should be fitted so as to provide a complete and co-ordinated system of protection for the electrical installation as a whole. The selection, arrangement and performance characteristics should be such that the following is achieved:

(i)　Maximum continuity of service to healthy circuits under fault conditions through the selective operation of the various protective devices.

(ii)　Rapid clearance of short-circuit faults in order to prevent consequential damage to the installation from fault currents.

(iii)　Protection of electrical equipment and circuits from damage due to overcurrents by co-ordination of the electrical characteristics of the circuit or apparatus and the tripping characteristics of the protective devices.

NOTE:　Generator protection should remain effective in the event of a substantial reduction of speed.

8.2　Short-circuit currents

(1)　AC systems

(i)　For evaluation of the prospective short-circuit current, the equivalent system impedance should be considered between the point of fault and the source of current, taking into account the subtransient, transient and steady state values, when necessary.

Due account should be taken of the fault current possible on line-earth and / or line-line-earth faults on systems where the neutral is solidly earthed or is earthed via a low impedance.

(ii)　The source of current should include the maximum number of generators which can be connected in parallel and the maximum number of motors which may be connected to them in normal service. The contribution of generators should be calculated on the basis of their characteristics.

(iii)　The contribution of induction motors, where precise information of their characteristics is lacking, may be taken as follows:

(a)　R.M.S. value of the a.c. components, expressed as a function of the rated current of the motors, I_n, this being the sum of the rated current of motors estimated to be normally simultaneously

34

in service:

— at the instant of short-circuit occurrence
(subtransient value)   6.25 I_n;
— after one cycle from short-circuit inception   2.5 I_n;
— after two cycles from short-circuit inception   1.0 I_n.

(b) The contribution of induction motors in determining the maximum peak value attainable by the short-circuit current should be taken as 8 I_n (value of current to be added to the maximum peak value of the short-circuit current from the generators).

(iv) The contribution of d.c. machines fed from solid state converters should be allowed for if transient inverter operation is likely to take place. Where precise information on their characteristics is lacking their contributions may be taken as 1.4 I_n (where I_n is the r.m.s. line current) at the instant of short circuit occurrence and may be neglected after the first half cycle.

(2)   DC systems

(i) The prospective short-circuit current at a definite point of the system should be evaluated by considering the equivalent system resistance between the point of fault and the source of current.

(ii) The source of current should include the maximum number of generators which can be connected in parallel. The maximum number of motors which may be simultaneously in service should also be included.

(iii) In the absence of precise information the following values should be assumed:

(a) 10 times full load current for generators;
(b) 6 times full load current for motors.

8.3   Choice of protective devices

(1)   Protection against short-circuit

(i) Protection against short-circuit should be provided by circuit-breakers or fuses.

(ii) The rated breaking capacity should be not less than the maximum prospective current to be broken at the point of installation.

(iii) The rated making capacity of every circuit-breaker or switch capable of being closed on a short-circuit, should be not less than the maximum peak value of prospective current at the point of installation.

NOTE: The voltage, the power factor (for a.c.), the time constant (for d.c.) and the time delay to which the rated breaking capacity is referred should be adequate for the most severe conditions.

35

(iv) The rated short-time current of every protective device should be adequate for the maximum short-circuit current which can occur at the point of installation allowing for the maximum duration permitted for the short-circuit.

(v) Integrally fused circuit-breakers should be regarded as having a making and breaking capacity equal to the certified fault capacity of the combination. Such circuit breakers should comply with BS 4752, Part 1.

(2) Protection against overload

(i) Circuit-breakers and other automatic switching devices used for overload protection should have a time / current characteristic adequate for the overload capacity of the circuit or equipment to be protected and should provide adequate discrimination.

(ii) Fuses with suitable characteristics may be used for overload protection.

8.4 Application of protective devices

(1) Short-circuit protection should be provided in each non-earthed line.

(2) Overload protection should be provided in each non-earthed line, except that it may be omitted in one line in each of the following circuits:

— insulated d.c. circuits;
— insulated single phase a.c. circuits;
— insulated three phase a.c. circuits with balanced loads;
— motors in accordance with 8.8(2), subject to the recommendations of 8.8(5).

(3) Protective devices should not interrupt earthed lines unless multipole circuit-breakers or switches are used which disconnect all lines simultaneously.

8.5 Generator protection

(1) Generators rated at less than 50 kW and not arranged for parallel operation may be protected by fuses and switches provided that the time / current characteristic of the fuses is matched to the overcurrent time / current characteristic of the generator.

(2) All other generators should be protected by circuit-breakers and in accordance with the following:

(i) AC generators
(a) The generator circuit-breaker should provide both overload and short-circuit protection. The current setting of the overload trip should not exceed 150% of the generator rating and the time delay should not exceed 15 seconds for continuous maximum rated (CMR) machines. For machines capable of sustained overload these figures

36

may be exceeded but the setting in terms of current and time delay should be such that the overload capacity of the generator is not exceeded.

(b) The current setting for short-circuit should be set below the maximum generator short-circuit current, the setting being at the lowest level of current which will co-ordinate with the trip settings of feeder breakers.

(c) When three or more generators operate in parallel account should be taken of fault current to be handled by the generator circuit-breakers in the event of a short-circuit on the generator side.

(ii) DC generators

(a) The generator circuit-breaker should provide both overload and short-circuit protection. The current setting of the overload trip should not exceed 150% of the generator rating and the time delay should not exceed 15 seconds for CMR machines. For machines capable of sustained overload these figures may be exceeded but the settings in terms of current and time delay should be such that the overload capacity of the generator is not exceeded.

(b) The current setting for short-circuit should be set below the maximum generator short-circuit current, to minimise damage to the machine. This trip should be set at the lowest value of current which will co-ordinate with the trip settings of feeder breakers.

(3)   Preference trips

To prevent any generator or its prime mover becoming overloaded, arrangements should be considered to shed sufficient load to ensure safe operation of the ship.

(4)   Reverse power / current protection

(i) AC generators arranged for parallel operation should be provided with time delayed reverse power protection. The arrangement should be selected and set in accordance with the characteristics of the prime mover.

A fall of 50% in the applied voltage should not render the reverse power device inoperative although it may alter the amount of reverse power required to operate the device and thereby open the breaker. The reverse power device may be replaced by other devices providing equivalent protection.

NOTE: The power to motor the prime mover may be taken as 2-6% of rating for turbines and 8-15% for diesel engines. A time delay of 5 seconds is generally suitable.

(ii) A d.c. generator arranged for parallel operation with other generators or with a storage battery should be provided with short time reverse current protection. The arrangement should be selected and set in accordance with the characteristics of the prime mover. A fall of 50% in the applied voltage should not render the reverse current device inoperative although it may alter the amount of reverse current required to operate the device and thereby open the breaker. When an equaliser connection is used the reverse current device should be connected in the pole opposite to that in which the series winding is connected.

(iii) The reverse current and / or power device should be capable of effectively handling reverse current emanating from the network, e.g. winches or cranes.

(5) Under-voltage protection

For generators arranged for parallel operation with one another or with an external power source feeder, means should be provided to prevent the closing of the generator breaker if the generator is not generating and to prevent the generator remaining connected to the busbars if the voltage collapses. If an under-voltage release is provided for this purpose the operation should be instantaneous when preventing closure of the breaker but should be delayed for discrimination purposes when tripping a breaker.

(6) Level compounded or 3-wire d.c. generators

For d.c. generators arranged to operate in parallel the following should be provided:

(i) For level compounded generators, an equaliser switch for each generator so interlocked that it closes before and opens after the contacts in the live poles of the circuit-breaker or alternatively a multipole circuit-breaker breaking all lines simultaneously.

(ii) In 3-wire systems, a switch in the middle wire so interlocked with the generator circuit-breaker connected to the outer lines as to operate simultaneously with them.

(7) Protection against internal faults is recommended for all large generating sets, e.g. greater than 1500 kW, particularly for the following fault conditions:

— stator winding to earth;
— stator winding phase to phase;
— excitation system failure.

(8) The over-current and time settings for generator circuit-breaker over-current devices and for "preference" tripping should be adjustable.

8.6 Protection of distribution circuits

(1) Each distribution circuit should be protected against overload and short-circuit by switches and fuses or by circuit-breakers, except as described

38

below:

(i) Where a final sub-circuit supplies a consuming device fitted with overload protection, only short-circuit protection is required for the sub-circuit.

(ii) The supply circuits to steering gear control systems should be provided with short-circuit protection only.

(2)   Interconnector cables that can be fed from both ends should be protected at each end.

8.7   The primary windings of transformers should be protected against short-circuit.

8.8   Motor protection

(1)   All motors exceeding 0.5 kW output should be individually protected against overload and short-circuit, except as provided in 8.8(2).

(2)   Motors for services essential to the safety and propulsion of the ship which are duplicated and supplied independently may have an overload alarm instead of overload protection. Steering gear motors should have an overload alarm instead of overload protection and the short-circuit protection should be for not less than twice the total rated load current of the motors in the circuit protected.

(3)   For continuously rated motors protective devices should have a time delay characteristic which ensures thermal protection of the motors under overload conditions and also permits the starting of the motors.

(4)   For intermittently rated motors the current / time characteristics of the device should be chosen with regard to actual service conditions of the motor.

(5)   In polyphase motor circuits adequate precautions should be taken to prevent damage due to single phasing. Motors driving steering gear power units should be provided with an audible and visual single phasing alarm located in a conspicuous position in the main machinery space or in the control room from which the machinery is normally controlled.

(6)   Motors rated above 0.5 kW should be provided with under voltage protection. See also 13.3. Motors driving steering gear power units should be arranged to re-start automatically when power is restored after a power failure.

8.9   Protection should be provided for instruments and pilot lamps preferably by current limiting devices such as fuses. These should be located as close to the source of power as practicable. The means of over-current protection for circuits containing earth-indicating lamps and pilot lamps should not be used for circuits containing voltmeters and voltage coils of instruments.

Exemption: A single means of protection may serve a device and an integral lamp provided that safe operation is not impaired.

NOTE: In control circuits such as those for:
— voltage regulators;
— circuit-breaker tripping control;
— electric propulsion control,
where operation of the protective device might introduce a hazard, protection may be omitted. If fuse protection is fitted the fuse rating should be relatively high, such that operation occurs only under short-circuit conditions.

8.10   Each lighting circuit should be protected against overload and short-circuit.

8.11   Where provision is made for temporary power supplies from an external source, a multipole circuit-breaker or multipole switch and fuses should be provided in the connection box to protect the feeder between the external power supply connection box and the main switchboard.

8.12   Storage batteries, other than engine starting batteries, should be provided with overload and short-circuit protection placed as near as practicable to the battery but outside the battery compartment. Batteries supplying emergency services should have short-circuit protection only. See also ~~14.13.~~ 14.12 (*)

8.13   Fuses

(1)   Fuses for the protection of circuits should comply with BS 88, or, for a.c. circuits only, with BS 3036, as applicable, and should be of the appropriate category defined therein.

(2)   ~~No fuse of rating less than 6 A need be inserted in any final sub-circuit.~~ final sub ccts fuses need not be rated at less than 6 A

(3)   Rewirable (semi-enclosed) fuses should not be used for distribution circuits.

SECTION 9

GENERATING PLANT AND MOTORS

Prime Movers

9.1 Prime movers should conform to the requirements of 1.2, 1.5, 1.10, 1.11 and 1.16. Electrical apparatus supplied with these prime movers should conform to the requirements of all relevant Sections of the Recommendations. Prime movers for driving generators should also comply with the requirements of the relevant British Standard:

    (i)   Steam turbines — BS 132
    (ii) Gas turbines   — BS 3135, BS 3863
    (iii) Oil engines   — BS 5514

9.2 The declared rating and overload capacity of prime movers should be compatible with the declared rating and specified overload (active kW) capacity of the driven generators. Where change in operating ambient conditions, see 1.10, may significantly alter the relationship between the capabilities of the prime mover and driven generator, appropriate measures should be employed to prevent damage.

9.3 Prime movers for driving electric generators intended for supplying essential services should be rated so that the electrical output to meet SOLAS requirements can be met under the relevant operating conditions in 1.10 and 1.11.

9.4 Governing characteristics

(1) Governors on prime movers should be such that they will automatically maintain rated speed within a momentary variation of 10% and a permanent variation not exceeding 5% when rated load is suddenly thrown off and when 50% load is suddenly thrown on followed after a short instant by the remaining 50% load.

Application of load in more than two load steps may be permitted provided that it is already catered for in the design stage.

The transient performance for all types of prime mover should at least meet the governing accuracy for Class A1 in BS 5514, Part 4.

(2) Each prime mover should be fitted with an emergency overspeed device which will operate at a speed not more than 15% above rated speed and has provision for tripping by hand. The design of the combined set should ensure that no damage will result from any overshoot after the emergency overspeed device has operated. The ability to withstand the maximum overshoot speed should be demonstrated during works performance tests.

41

(3)   For a.c. generating sets operating in parallel, the governing characteristics of the prime movers should be such that within the limits of 20% and 100% total kW load, the load on any generating set does not normally differ from its proportionate share of the total kW load by more than 15% of the rated output of the largest machine or 25% of the rating of the individual machine in question. The facilities for adjusting the governor at normal frequencies should be sufficiently fine to permit a minimum adjustment of load on the prime mover not exceeding 5% of the rated kW load. The governor setting should be capable of adjustment both locally and from a remote switchboard.

9.5   Cyclic irregularity

The maximum permissible cyclic irregularity in a reciprocating engine through one engine cycle should conform to the following:

(i)   For an engine having one or two cylinders, the cyclic irregularity should not be worse than 1/75th unless a closer limit is specified.
(ii) For an engine having more than two cylinders, the cyclic irregularity should not be worse than the values given in Table 9.1.

Table 9.1   Limits of Cyclic Irregularity

Number of engine impulses per second (f)	Cyclic irregularity to be not worse than
Up to 4	1/150
6	1/220
8 to 20	$\dfrac{1}{\dfrac{2000}{f} - f}$
Above 20	1/75

NOTE: Cyclic irregularity is defined as the ratio of the maximum variation in angular velocity at the flywheel during one engine cycle to the mean angular velocity when the engine is running at any load up to and including rated load and at rated speed. This is conveniently expressed as follows:

$$\frac{\text{Max. speed} - \text{Min. speed}}{\text{Mean speed}}$$

9.6   Each combined prime mover, transmission system and generator should be designed to withstand without damage the effects of the most onerous short-circuit condition at the generator terminals when running at rated voltage and speed.If it can be demonstrated that temporary loss of generating plant will not affect the safety of the ship or its plant, then alternative proposals may be accepted.In such cases an acceptable proposal may be a quickly replaceable shaft, purposely designed to shear without other resultant damage.

NOTE: It is recognised that damage to the commutator / brushgear of
d.c. generators may result from conditions of short-circuit.

9.7   Lubrication

(1)   Prime movers should be efficiently and continuously lubricated at all running speeds and at all working oil temperatures without the spilling of oil, with the ship at the inclinations from normal as specified in 1.11.

(2)   Generating sets dependent on forced lubrication should be arranged to shut down automatically on failure of lubrication.

9.8   The normal speed of a combined generating set should not be in the vicinity of a critical speed.

9.9   Where a turbine-driven d.c. generator is arranged to run in parallel with other generators, a switch should be fitted on each turbine emergency overspeed device to open the generator circuit-breaker when the emergency overspeed device functions. The contacts of the overspeed switch should be normally closed.

Generators and motors

9.10   Motors and ships' service generators, including their exciters, should comply with BS 2949 and, generally, unless inappropriate, they should be suitable for continuous duty at their rated load for an unlimited period without the specified limits of temperature rise being exceeded. Where continuous rating is inappropriate, generators and motors should be assigned ratings to BS 4999 or IEC 34-1 in accordance with their specified duty. When tested under load conditions corresponding to an assigned rating the specified temperature rise should not be exceeded.

9.11   Machines should be so constructed that when running at any and every working speed all revolving parts are well balanced and they should be capable of withstanding over-speeds required by the prime mover.

9.12   Consideration should be given in the design of d.c. machines and their protective system to means of minimising damage in the event of short-circuit.

43

9.13   Consideration should be given to provide effective means to prevent accumulation of moisture and condensation within the machines, especially when they are idle for appreciable periods, for example, by means of space heaters.

9.14   Every sleeve bearing should be fitted with an inspection cover and means for visual indication of level or flow or pressure, as appropriate to the type of lubrication employed.

9.15   All machines should be so designed and located that adequate space is provided to produce efficient cable terminations. See also 1.18.

9.16   Adjustment of generator voltage

(1)   Where manual adjustment of terminal voltage is necessary or is provided for the satisfactory operation of generators, the facilities should be provided at the switchboard or at an appropriate control position.

(2)   For each generator, coupled to its prime mover at any permissible temperature within the working range, the means provided should be capable of adjusting the voltage at any load between no-load and full-load to within:

  (i)   0.5% of rated voltage for generators of rating exceeding 100 kW; or
  (ii) 1.0% of rated voltage for generators of rating not exceeding 100 kW.

9.17   The design of excitation systems, including automatic voltage regulator, if used, should be of a type suitable for shipboard conditions, and be capable of operating under all specified conditions of steady and transient load including short-circuit.
    The components of the excitation system, including automatic voltage regulator, if used, should be of a type suitable for shipboard conditions, and be capable of operating under all specified conditions of steady and transient load including short-circuit.

9.18   When it is intended that two or more a.c. generators will be operated in parallel means should be provided to divide the reactive power proportionally between the generators.The sharing shall not differ by more than 10% of the rated reactive output of the largest machine or 25% of the smallest machine, whichever is the lesser.

9.19   The excitation system provided in accordance with 9.16 should also comply with 9.19(1) to 9.19(3).

(1)   Each a.c. generator for ships' service should be provided with an excitation system capable of maintaining the voltage under steady state conditions within plus or minus 2.5% of rated voltage for all loads between zero and rated load within the range of power factor likely to be encountered in the ship e.g. 0.5 to Unity, when driven by its prime mover.

(2)   Under steady short-circuit conditions the current should be

maintained at not less than three times its rated value for 2 seconds or such other figures which ensure correct operation of the protective system.

(3)   Emergency sets, which are required to meet the same general requirements as in 9.1, need only maintain the steady-state voltage within plus or minus 3.5% and during transient conditions to recover its voltage within plus or minus 4% in not more than 5 seconds.

9.20   If generators are intended to run with their neutrals solidly connected together, or connected via a low impedance, the manufacturer(s) should be informed so that the generators can be designed to have a low value of harmonic voltage and / or to operate with the resulting circulating currents. This is particularly important if they are of different designs.

NOTE 1 This condition can arise during synchronising even if they do not run continuously with neutrals inter-connected.

NOTE 2 If generator neutrals are inter-connected provision may have to be made for the resultant circulating currents in the machine design and in the protection system, particularly during the period of the synchronisation and before the kW load is shared.

NOTE 3 If the generators are intended to have their neutrals earthed or inter-connected, means should be provided to isolate each generator winding for test and maintenance purposes.

9.21   For every a.c. motor, the starting current and its duration should be compatible with the mechanical load, the overall characteristics of the supply system and the protective equipment.
Each motor should be rated in accordance with its duty.

Shaft Generator Systems

9.22   General

The requirements of 9.23 to 9.26 relate to generators driven from the propulsion plant and include the generators, synchronous compensators, prime movers, transmissions, excitation circuits, semiconductor convertors and control equipment.

9.23   Performance

(1)   Shaft generator systems should conform to the requirements of 9.10 to 9.15 inclusive.

(2)   Semiconductor convertors forming part of the shaft generator system should conform to the requirements of Section 17.

45

(3)   Where shaft generator systems are to operate in parallel with ship's service generators, they should conform to the requirements of 9.16 to 9.20.

(4)   The design of the propulsion shaft system including, where applicable, separate power take-off drives for generators should be such as to avoid damaging torsional stress and vibration.

(5)   The electrical system should be stable under all operating conditions within the specified range of shaft speed variations and specified speed variation periods.

(6)   The capability of the prime mover(s) propeller shaft systems and seating should be adequate to withstand the effects of the most onerous short-circuit conditions at the generator terminals when running at rated voltage and speed.

9.24   Construction

(1)   A generator mounted in, or connected to, the propeller shaft line should have adequate clearances in normal running, and under fault conditions, to avoid damage from dimensional variations as a result of ship structural flexing.

(2)   Lubrication should be effective at all operating speeds. Where creep speeds can occur, e.g. with turbine drives, see 25.4(6).

9.25   Additional requirements for generating systems in which the shaft generators form part of the main source of power required by SOLAS should also comply with 9.25(1) to 9.25(4).

(1)   The generating system should be capable of continuously delivering the power required to meet SOLAS requirements under all ship manoeuvring conditions including propeller being stopped.

(2)   The generating system should not be less effective and reliable than independent generating sets.

(3)   The generating system should be such as to ensure that with any one generator or its prime mover out of operation, the remaining generator(s) will be capable of providing electrical services necessary to start the main propulsion plant from a dead ship condition.

(4)   The emergency generator may be used for the purpose of starting from a dead ship condition if its capability, either alone or subsequently combined with that of any other generator, is sufficient to provide at the same time the emergency services required by the Appropriate Authority.

9.26   Other shaft generators

Generators driven from the propulsion plant which do not comply with 9.25

may be used as additional source(s) of power with respect to the power balance, but attention should be given to a quick restoration of electrical power to all auxiliaries necessary for maintaining the ship in operational and safe conditions after an electrical power interruption, e.g. due to a sudden stop of the propulsion plant. The time involved for restoring the above mentioned services should be agreed between the manufacturer and purchaser.

SECTION 10

CONSTRUCTION OF CABLES

10.1 General

(1)   Cables of materials and construction differing from those covered by the Standards referred to in 10.2 and 10.3 are not precluded when such materials and construction are acceptable to the Appropriate Authority.

(2)   Certain standards nominate solid wire for conductor sizes up to and including 2.5 mm^2. Where design conditions require stranded conductors they should be selected from BS 6360.

(3)   The cross sectional area of a conductor should be not less than 0.5 mm^2. See Section 2 regarding earthing conductors.

(4)   Where a screen is applied over the insulated core, pair, triple or quad and / or applied overall in the case of multicore, multipair, multitriple, or multiquad, such screen(s) should be one of the following types:

  (i)   braid(s) of tinned copper wires;
  (ii) composite polyester / metal laminate tape applied helically with a tinned copper drain wire in contact with the metallic side of the tape. The drain wire cross sectional area should be 0.5 mm^2 minimum and with a minimum of 7 wires.

(5)   All cables should be of the 'flame-retardant' type and should, as a minimum, comply with the performance requirements of BS 4066, Part 1. For the performance of cable installed in bunches consideration should be given to the use of the appropriate category of BS 4066, Part 3. Particular attention is drawn to the Foreword of this Standard. See also 11.6(2).

(6)   Where cables are required to be 'fire resisting' in addition to being flame-retardant, they should, as a minimum, comply with the performance requirements of IEC 331.
  For the performance of cables under specific conditions reference should be made to BS 6387 which includes tests to determine cable performance during impact and water deluge in fire situations:

  C — resistance to fire alone;
  W — resistance to fire with water;
  Z — resistance to fire with mechanical shock.

See also 11.17(1).

(7)   Non-magnetic materials should be provided for any armouring required for single-core cables to be used in a.c. circuits.

(8)   The shape of the cable shall be such that the degree of protection specified is maintained. See also 11.9.

10.2   Cables rated up to 1000 volts

Cables for propulsion, power, lighting, controls, signalling and communications should have copper conductors and should be constructed in accordance with one of the following standards:

BS 5308   Instrumentation cables

BS 5467   Armoured cables with thermosetting insulation for electricity supply

BS 6004*   PVC-insulated cables (non-armoured) for electric power and lighting

BS 6207   Mineral-insulated copper-sheathed cables with copper conductors

BS 6346*   PVC-insulated cables for electricity supply

BS 6724*   Armoured cables for electricity supply having thermosetting insulation with low emission of smoke and corrosive gases when affected by fire

* These standards nominate solid wire conductors up to and including 2.5 mm^2. See 10.1(2).

BS 6883   Elastomer-insulated cables for fixed wiring in ships

IEC 92-3   Cables (construction, testing and installations)

IEC 92-350 Low voltage shipboard power cables. General construction and test requirements

IEC 92-353 Single and multicore cables with extruded solid insulation for voltages 0.6 / 1 kV

IEC 92-374 Shipboard telecommunication cables and radio frequency cables. Telephone cables for non-essential communication services

IEC 92-375 Shipboard telecommunication cables and radio frequency cables. General instrumentation, control and communication cables

IEC 92-376   Shipboard multicore cables for control circuits

IEC 502   Extruded solid dielectric insulated power cables for rated voltages from 1 kV to 30 kV. (This publication also covers 0.6 / 1 kV cables)

10.3   Cables rated at above 1000 volts

Cables for operation above 1000 volts should have copper conductors and be constructed in accordance with one of the following Standards:

BS 5467   Armoured cables with thermosetting insulation for electricity supply

BS 6346   PVC-insulated cables for electricity supply

BS 6622   Cables with extruded cross-linked polyethylene or ethylene propylene rubber insulation for rated voltages from 3 800 / 6 600 V up to 19 000 / 33 000 V (limited to 8 700 / 15 000 volts)

BS 6724   Armoured cables for electricity supply having thermosetting insulation with low emission of smoke and corrosive gases when affected by fire

BS 6883   Elastomeric insulated cables for fixed wiring in ships

IEC 502   Extruded solid dielectric insulated power cables for rated voltages from 1 kV to 30 kV (limited to 8 700 / 15 000 volts)

10.4   Cables for special applications

For guidance on cables for special applications reference should be made to 11.17 which gives full details of applications and recommended cable types and specifications.

10.5   Cable material types

For guidance on types of materials used in the construction of cables see Table 10.1. It is not intended that this Table be used for cable selection without reference to the applicable cable standard, and the list of materials given therein is not meant to be exhaustive.

Table 10.1   Cable Material Types

Thermoplastic Insulations	Temperature Classification
Polyethylene BS 6234 Type 03 *amended*	60°C
PVC BS 6746 Type TI1 General Purpose Type TI2 Flexible Type 4 Flexible Type 5 Hard	70°C 70°C 85°C 85°C
PVC IEC 92-351 Type PVC / A	60°C
Thermoplastic-Sheaths	
Polyethylene BS 6234 Type 03C	60°C
PVC BS 6746 Type TM1 Hard Type TM2 General Purpose Flexible Type 4 Flexible Type 5 Hard Type 6 General Purpose Type 7 For RF cables to BS 2316 Type 8 For RF cables to BS 2316 Type 9 For cables with maximum conductor temperature of	70°C 70°C 85°C 85°C 70°C 70°C 70°C 90°C
PVC IEC 92-359 Type ST1 Type ST2	60°C 85°C
Thermosetting Insulations (Rubbers including Elastomerics)	
BS 6899 Type GP1 Typically EPR or EPDM for 600 / 1000 V operation Type GP2 Typically EPR or EPDM for higher voltages Type GP4 Typically EPR or EPDM for 600 / 1000 V operation Type GP5 Typically EPR or EPDM for higher voltages Type GP8 XLPE Type E12 Silicone rubber	85°C 85°C 90°C 90°C 90°C 150°C
IEC 92-351 EPR XLPE S95 Silicone rubber	85°C 85°C 95°C
Thermosetting Sheath	
BS 6899 Type RS3 Typically ordinary duty CSP or CPE (GP HOFR) Type RS4 Typically heavy duty CSP or CPE (HD HOFR)	85°C 85°C
IEC 92-359 Type SE1 Typically PCP Type SH1 Typically CSP or CPE	85°C 85°C

SECTION 11

SELECTION AND INSTALLATION OF CABLES

11.1 General

AC wiring should be carried out, as far as is reasonably practical, in twin or multicore cables. Where it is necessary to use single-core cables in a.c. circuits special precautions may be necessary.

11.2 Rated voltage of cables

(1) The voltage rating of any cable should be not less than the nominal voltage of the circuit for which it is used.Cables may be used on circuits where the nominal voltage exceeds the rated power-frequency voltage between conductors (U) but in no case shall the nominal voltage exceed the highest system voltage (U_m).

(2) Careful consideration should be given to cables subjected to voltage surges associated with highly inductive circuits to ensure that they are of a suitable voltage rating.

11.3 Rated operating temperature of cables

The rated operating temperatures of the cables should be at least 10°C higher than the maximum ambient temperatures likely to exist, or to be produced, in the space where the cable is installed.

> NOTE: The rated operating temperature for cables can be obtained by reference to the Tables in Section 12.

11.4 Determination of the cross-sectional areas of conductors

(1) Every conductor of a cable, flexible cable or flexible cord should be capable of carrying the maximum current which will normally flow through it, without exceeding the appropriate current rating given in Section 12, determined by application of the correction factors for ambient temperature and grouping.
In assessing the normal maximum current, account may be taken of any diversity factors that are applicable. See also Section 3.

(2) Where more than six cables are bunched together, a correction factor of 0.85 is to be applied.

(3) For the purposes of determining the sizes of conductors in lighting

52

circuits every lampholder should be deemed to require a current equivalent to the maximum load likely to be connected to it. In the absence of precise data this should be assumed to be at least 100 W in the case of incandescent lamps.For low voltage discharge and fluorescent luminaries, see 15.17.

Where socket outlets are connected into a final lighting sub-circuit the maximum loading for each outlet should be assumed to be 500 W.

(4)   The cross-sectional area of conductors should be sufficient to ensure that at no point in the installation will the voltage between the conductors comprising a circuit fall more than 6% below the nominal voltage, when the said conductors are carrying the maximum current under their normal conditions of service. For supplies from batteries with a voltage not exceeding 50 volts, this value may be increased to 10%.

Under special conditions of short duration, such as motor starting, higher voltage drops may be accepted providing that the operation of connected equipment is not adversely affected.

(5)   In motor circuits, the effects of starting, and frequency thereof, should be considered to ensure that the rated operating temperature of the associated supply cable(s) is not exceeded.

(6)   Where cables are connected in parallel they should be of the same type and length and should have conductors of the same cross-section and be arranged so as to carry substantially equal current.

The current carrying capacity (I_p) of parallel connected cables should be based on the following formulae:

(i)   For twin and multicore cables and single-core cables in trefoil $I_p = I \times n$.

(ii) For other single-cored cables: $I_p = 0.9I \times n$.

Where: I = current rating as determined by 11.4(1) and 11.4(2);
        n = number of parallel connected conductors.

(7)   After having been determined by the foregoing, the cross-sectional area should be checked to ensure the cables and their insulated conductors are capable of withstanding the mechanical and thermal effects of the maximum short-circuit current which can flow in any part of the circuit in which they are installed. This should take into consideration not only the time / current characteristics of the circuit protective device, but also the peak value of the prospective short-circuit current during the first half-cycle.

(8)   Where the load is non-continuous the appropriate non-continuous rating table in Section 12 should be used.It should be ensured that the cable still conforms with 11.4(4), 11.4(5), 11.4(6) and 11.4(7).

(9)   Every equaliser connection for use with compound wound generators should have a cross-sectional area of at least 50% of the cross-sectional area of the positive or negative connections to the generator.

(10) For polyphase circuits in which serious imbalance is unlikely to be sustained in normal service, other than discharge lighting, a reduced neutral conductor may be used. However, in all cases the neutral conductor should have a cross-sectional area of at least 50% of the cross-sectional area of the phase conductor.

(11) The mechanical strength of conductors should be sufficient to withstand the handling which the cable will be subjected to during its installation and the working conditions when it is in service.

11.5 Protective covering of cables

(1) Cables fitted on decks or in areas exposed to weather, in damp and wet situations, in machinery compartments and, in general, where water condensation or harmful vapours (including oil vapour) may be present, should have the conductor insulating materials enclosed in an impervious sheath.

> NOTE 1   As a guide, PVC, PCP, CSP and CPE sheaths are considered as "impervious" in this context, although not suitable for permanent immersion in liquids, see 11.17(10) and 11.17(11).

> NOTE 2   Certain cable types referred to in Section 10, e.g. BS 6724, are intended primarily for installation in air in dry environments.

(2) In instances where the construction of a cable does not conform with a Standard referred to in Section 10, it should be ensured that the materials of the protective sheath are compatible with those of the conductor insulation, with the intended operating temperature of the conductor insulation and with the intended environment.

(3) The mechanical strength of the protective covering should be sufficient to withstand the handling which the cable will be subjected to during its installation and the working conditions when it is in service.If the protective covering is considered inadequate, the cable should be fitted in pipes or conduit or trunking, or be otherwise protected, e.g. by metal braid or armour.

(4) The metallic screen, sheath, braid or armour of a cable exposed to damp situations or harmful vapours should be protected by an overall impervious sheath, alternatively, such screens, sheaths, braids or armour should be of corrosion resistant material.

11.6 Cable runs

(1) Cables should, as far as is practicable, be fixed in accessible positions.

(2) Cable runs should be so arranged as to prevent, as far as is practical, the propagation of fire.

(3)   The construction of cable runs should take account of the need for protection against destructive pests or rodents.

(4)   Cables having insulating materials with different maximum permissible conductor temperatures should not be bunched in a common clip, support, gland, conduit, trunking or duct.
Where this is impracticable, those cables with higher permissible conductor temperatures should be derated to ensure that their operating temperature is not greater than that of the lowest temperature rated cable in the bunch.
Cables for control circuits may, however, be bunched with power cables having higher permissible conductor temperatures, providing that the temperature within the bunch does not exceed the permissible temperature of the control cable sheath.

(5)   Cables having a protective covering which may damage the covering of more vulnerable cables should not be bunched with the latter in a common clip, support, gland, conduit, trunking or duct.

(6)   Cables having a bare metallic screen, sheath, braid or armour should be installed in such a way that galvanic corrosion by contact with other metals is prevented.

   NOTE 1   An impervious sheath will prevent the armour of different cables coming into contact.

   NOTE 2   Impervious sheaths should be maintained intact to exclude the ingress of water.

(7)   Cable runs should be selected so as to avoid action from condensed moisture or drip. Cables should, as far as possible, be remote from sources of heat, such as boilers, hot pipes, resistors, etc., and protected from avoidable risks of mechanical damage. Where installation of cables near sources of heat cannot be avoided, and where there is consequently a risk of damage to the cables by heat, suitable shields should be installed, or other precautions to avoid overheating should be taken, for example, use of special ventilation, installation of heat insulating materials, or use of special heat resistant cables.

(8)   Cables should not be installed across expansion joints. Where this is unavoidable, a loop of cable having a length proportioned to the expansion of the joint should be provided. The minimum internal radius of the loop during installation should not be less than 12 times the external diameter of the cable.

(9)   The internal radius of bend for the installation of cables for fixed wiring should be chosen according to the type of cable and should be not less than the values given in Table 11.1 and Table 11.2.

(10)   For services with duplicate supplies, the two supply lines should follow different paths, which should be separated as far as reasonably practical.

55

Table 11.1 Minimum internal radii of bends in cables rated up to 1000 volts

Cable construction		Overall diameter	Minimum internal radius of bend (times overall diameter of cable)
Insulation/conductors 1	Finish 2	3	4
Thermoplastic or thermosetting / circular conductors	Unarmoured	Not exceeding 10 mm	3
		Exceeding 10 mm but not exceeding 25 mm	4
	Wire braid armoured	Not exceeding 25 mm	4
	Wire braid armoured and unarmoured	Exceeding 25 mm	6
	Spiral steel wire armoured	Any	6
	Composite polyester / metal laminate tape screened or collective tape screening	Any	8
Thermoplastic or thermosetting / shaped conductors	Any	Any	8
Mineral	Any	Any	6

Table 11.2 Minimum internal radii of bends in cables rated at above 1000 volts*

Cable construction		Overall diameter	Minimum internal radius of bend (times overall diameter of cable)
Insulation/conductors 1	Finish 2	3	4
Thermoplastic or thermosetting / circular conductors	Unarmoured and unscreened	Not exceeding 25 mm	4
		Exceeding 25 mm	6
	Wire braid screened or armoured, spiral steel wire armoured or metal sheathed	Any	6
Thermoplastic or thermosetting / shaped conductors	Any	Any	8

* For high voltage cables operating on 6 kV systems and above, a minimum internal radius of bend of 12 times overall diameter of cable should be used and, where these cables are screened, either the bend should be carefully controlled using a former or a bend larger than the minimum radii should be used.

57

(11)   Cables and wiring for main and emergency power, lighting, internal communications or signalling should, so far as is practical, be routed clear of galleys, machinery spaces and other high fire risk areas, except for supplying equipment in those spaces.

(12)   Where possible cables should be run in such a manner as to preclude their being rendered unserviceable by heating of the bulkhead caused by fire in an adjacent compartment.

(13)   Special attention should be given to the protection of main cable routes passing between machinery spaces and control areas.

11.7   Mechanical protection

(1)   In situations where there could be a risk of mechanical damage, cables should be enclosed in suitable conduits or casings, unless the cable covering (for example, armour or sheath) provides adequate protection.

(2)   In situations where there would be an exceptional risk of mechanical damage, for example, in storage spaces, cables should be protected by steel casing, trunking or conduits, even when armoured, if the ships structure or attached parts do not afford sufficient protection to the cables.Any metal casing used should be sufficiently protected against corrosion.

11.8   Support / fixings

(1)   With the exception of cables for portable appliances and those installed in pipes, conduits, trunking or special casings, cables should be fixed by means of clips, saddles or staps of suitable flame-retardant material and arranged so that the cables remain tight without their coverings being damaged.

(2)   The distances between supports should be chosen according to the type of cable and the probability of vibration and should not exceed 400 mm. For a horizontal cable run, fixings should be provided to restrain the cable movement where the cables are laid on cable supports in the form of tray or plates, separate support brackets, hangers or ladder rack fixings. The spacings between the fixing points may be up to 900 mm, provided that there are supports with maximum spacing as specified above. This relaxation should not be applied to cable runs on decks or in areas which can be subjected to forces of seawater impingement.
    If the cables are installed below cable ways or supports, the fixing distances for securing the cable should be in accordance with those given in Table 11.3.

(3)   The cable supports and accessories should be robust and constructed from corrosion resistant material or suitably treated to resist corrosion. Low melting point metals or alloys, e.g. aluminium, should not be used.

(4)   Cable clips or straps made from a material other than metal (such as polyamide, PVC, etc.) may be used.

NOTE: Attention should be paid to the suitability of these materials with regard to low temperature and other environmental conditions.

Table 11.3   Maximum spacing of clips for securing cables

Overall diameter of cable	Wire braid armoured & unarmoured cables	Spiral steel wire armoured cables	Mineral insulated copper sheathed cables*
1	2	3	4
	mm	mm	mm
Not exceeding 8 mm	200	250	300
Exceeding 8 mm and not exceeding 13 mm	250	300	370
Exceeding 13 mm and not exceeding 20 mm	300	350	450
Exceeding 20 mm and not exceeding 30 mm	350	400	450
Exceeding 30 mm	400	450	—

The spacings given in this Table are applicable to horizontal runs: for vertical runs they may be increased by 25%.

* Where mineral insulated copper sheathed cables are spaced away from bulkheads the spacings of clips should be in accordance with Column 3.

NOTE: When designing a cable support system for single-core cables consideration should also be given to the effects of the electrodynamic forces developing on the occurrence of a short-circuit. The distances between cable supports detailed in Table 11.3 may not be adequate for these cables.

(5)   When cables are fixed by means of clips or straps referred to in 11.8(4) and these cables are not laid on top of horizontal trays or cable supports, suitable metal clips or saddles should be added at regular distances, e.g. 1 m to 3 m, in order to prevent the release of cables during a fire. This also applies to the fixing of non-metallic conduits or pipes.

NOTE: This does not necessarily apply in the case of cable runs with only one or a few cables of small diameter for the connection of a luminaire, alarm transducer, etc.

(6)   Cables should be so installed that the stress applied to them either by reason of their own weight or for any other reason is minimised. These precautions are particularly important for cables of small cross-section and for cables on vertical runs, or in vertical pipes. Such cables should be suitably supported.

11.9   Cables penetrating bulkheads and decks

(1)   Penetration of watertight decks and bulkheads should be effected in a watertight manner. Either individual glands, multi-transit assemblies, or boxes containing several cables and filled with a flame-retardant packing may be used for this purpose. Whichever type of cable is used, the glands, transits or boxes and their packing should be such that the assembly meets the requirements of the Appropriate Authority.

> NOTE: Care should be taken in choosing packings to avoid cables being adversely affected, e.g. by high temperature arising from the pouring of the compound, chemical reaction with cable sheath, etc.

(2)   Where cables pass through watertight bulkheads care should be taken with the glanding arrangements to prevent "cold flow" which may occur due to compression of the cable.

(3)   Where cables pass through non-watertight bulkheads, beams or other steel structure, the holes through which they pass should be glanded or bushed with suitable materials, where necessary, to avoid damage to the cables.

(4)   The materials used for glands or bushes should be such that there is no risk of corrosion or damage to the cables or to the steel structure.

(5)   Where cables pass through bulkheads or decks, arrangements should be such that the integrity of the bulkhead or deck is not impaired, see 11.6(2).

11.10   Installation in metallic pipes, conduits or trunking

(1)   Conduits and conduit fittings for use therewith should, with the exception of inspection and draw-in boxes, see 11.10(2), conform in all respects to BS 4568, Parts 1 and 2, as applicable, and should be heavy gauge and welded or solid drawn. Steel pipes should comply with BS 1387 and be threaded in accordance with BS 21.

(2)   Inspection and draw-in boxes should be of metal and should be in rigid electrical and mechanical connection with the conduits. The boxes should, in addition, conform to BS 4568, Parts 1 and 2, so far as is applicable.

60

For steel conduits or pipes this connection should be obtained by screwing into the box or into a device clamping both sides of the wall of the box.

(3)   Pipes, conduits and trunking should have a suitable corrosion-resistant finish, inside and out.

(4)   The ends of pipes, conduits or trunking should be reamed, shaped or bushed in such a way as to avoid damage to the cables.

(5)   The internal dimensions and the radii of any bends in pipes, conduits or trunking should be such as to enable any cables to be readily drawn in or out. The maximum number and sizes of cables installed in pipes, conduit or trunking should be such that a space factor of 40% is not exceeded. The internal radius of any bend should be not less than those permitted for cable, see 11.6(9). For pipes exceeding 63 mm external diameter the internal radius should be not less than twice the external diameter of the pipe.

> NOTE: The space factor above applies to installations where the cables are not drawn round more than two 90° bends conforming to BS 4568, Parts 1 and 2, as applicable; where there are more than two such bends, an appropriate reduction in the number of cables drawn should be made.

(6)   If necessary, ventilating openings should be provided, preferably at the highest and lowest points, so as to permit air circulation and to obviate the possibility of water accumulation in any part of the pipe, conduit or trunking run. Such arrangements should not in any way jeopardise any required degree of fire integrity.

(7)   Where there is a risk of a pipe, conduit or trunking breaking because of its length, appropriate expansion joints should be provided.

(8)   Where cables are to be drawn into pipes, conduits or trunking, draw-in boxes should be installed, where necessary, in order to ensure that the cables are not damaged during installation.

(9)   All pipes, conduits and trunking should be earthed and should be electrically continuous across all joints.

11.11   Installation in non-metallic pipes, conduits, trunking, ducts or capping and casing

Cables may be installed in non-metallic pipes, conduits, trunking, ducts or casings either on the surface or concealed behind ceilings or panelling subject to the requirements of 11.11(1) to 11.11(7).

(1)   Conduits, pipes and trunking should be of non-hygroscopic material and be flame-retardant in accordance with the principles of performance tests of BS 4066, Part 1. Capping and casing should be made flame-retardant to Class 1 surface spread of flame test, BS 476, Part 7.

(2)   Non-metallic pipes, conduits or trunking should not be installed in areas open to the weather or in refrigerated spaces or other locations if they would be liable to be damaged if exposed to extremes of temperature.

(3)   Joints in and terminations of pipes and conduits should be made by screwing or otherwise firmly anchoring.

(4)   In situations where pipes, conduits or trunking are liable to mechanical damage they should be provided with suitable protection.

(5)   If necessary to prevent movement in trunking or casings, cables should be clipped, see 11.8.

Metal clips or saddles are to be used at frequent intervals in order to prevent non-metallic pipes, conduits or trunking and the cable therein dropping in the case of fire.

(6)   If the fixing of the capping is by means of screws, such screws should be of non-rusting material arranged in such a manner to avoid damage to the cables. The capping should be readily accessible.

(7)   All installations in non-metallic piping, conduits or trunking should also comply with 11.10(6).

11.12   Cable ends

(1)   The ends of every conductor should be securely terminated by means which contain all the strands of the conductor.

(2)   The ends of every conductor having a nominal cross-sectional area exceeding 2.5 mm^2 should be provided with soldering sockets or with compression type sockets or be connected by means of substantial mechanical clamps. Cable sockets and clamps should be of such dimensions and design that the maximum current likely to flow through them will not cause the rated operating temperature of the cable insulation to be exceeded.

(3)   The means of fixing of conductors and terminals should be capable of withstanding the thermal and dynamic effects of short-circuits.

(4)   Soldering fluxes containing acid or other corrosive substances should not be used.

(5)   At the ends of cables, the insulation should not be removed farther than is necessary having regard to the type of termination used. The braid, metal sheath, or other covering over the insulation including the tape (if any) in contact therewith, should be cut back at least 13 mm from the end of the insulation in cables up to 13 mm diameter (measured over the insulation) and at least 25 mm from the end of the insulation in cables of greater diameter. The covering over the insulation should not be cut back beyond the point of entry to the terminal box or fitting.

NOTE: The dimensions referred to above do not apply to mineral insulated metal sheathed cables.

62

(6)   The ends of mineral insulated metal sheathed cables should be so sealed as to prevent the ingress of moisture. Such sealing materials and any material used to insulate the conductors where they emerge from the insulation should have adequate insulating and moisture proofing properties and should retain these properties throughout the range of temperatures to which the cable is to be subjected in service.

(7)   Where cable cores are not colour or number coded the cores should be marked for identification at their ends.

11.13   Earthing of braids, armour and metallic sheaths of cables

See Section 2.

11.14   Cable joints, tappings (branch circuits) and joint boxes

(1)   Joints

Cable runs should not normally include joints. If, in the case of repair or due to sectional construction arrangements, a joint is necessary, the joint should be of such a type that the electrical continuity, insulation, mechanical strength, earthing and flame-retardant or fire resisting characteristics are not less than those required for the cables. The conductor joints should preferably be of the in-line crimped type in accordance with BS 4579, Part 1. See also 11.14(3). Separate mechanical protection may be required.
    Joints should be clearly marked to indicate the cable(s) and core(s).

(2)   Tappings (branch circuits)

Tappings (branch circuits) may be used providing that the jointing components are of suitable design and are appropriate for the voltage and current ratings of the circuits.
    The design should also ensure that the conductors remain suitably insulated and protected from mechanical damage and environmental action. See also 11.14(3). The conductor cross section is to be maintained unless the branch is fitted with a fuse.
    Tappings should be clearly marked to identify the cable(s) and core(s).

(3)   Joint boxes

Joint boxes used for cable joints or tappings should have the live parts mounted on durable, flame-retardant, moisture-resistant materials of high dielectric strength and high insulation resistance.
    Live parts should be so arranged by suitable spacing, or shielding with flame-retardant insulating material, that a short-circuit cannot readily occur between conductors of a different polarity or between conductors and earthed metal.
    Joint boxes should be made of flame-retardant material and they should be clearly identified defining their function and voltage.

11.15   Installation of single-core cables for a.c. distribution

(1)   The cables should be either non-armoured or they should be armoured with non-magnetic material.

(2)   Conductors belonging to the same circuit should be contained within the same pipe, conduit or trunking. Clamps which fix such conductors should include all the phases, unless they are made of non-magnetic material.

(3)   In the installing of two, three of four single-core cables forming respectively single-phase circuits, three-phase circuits or three-phase and neutral circuits the cables should, as far as possible, be in contact with one another.

In every case the distance measured between the external covering of two adjacent cables, should not be greater than one cable diameter.

(4)   When single-core cables having a current rating greater than 250 A must be installed near a steel bulkhead, the clearance between the cables and the bulkhead should be at least 50 mm, unless the cables belonging to the same a.c. circuit are installed in trefoil formation.

(5)   Magnetic materials should not be used between single-core cables of a group. Where cables pass through steel bulkheads, all the conductors of the same circuit should pass through a plate or gland, so made that there is no magnetic material between the cables, and the clearance between the cables and the magnetic material should be not less than 75 mm, unless the cables belonging to the same a.c. circuit are installed in trefoil formation.

(6)   In circuits involving several single-core cables in parallel per phase, all cables should follow the same route and have the same cross-sectional area.

When cables of a conductor cross-sectional area of 185 mm^2 or over are employed for three-phase circuits greater than 30 metres in length they should be installed in trefoil formation in order to equalise the impedance.

11.16   Installation in refrigeration spaces

(1)   Cables to be installed in refrigeration spaces should be protected against mechanical damage. Cables insulated or sheathed with PVC should not be used in refrigerated spaces unless the relevant PVC compounds are appropriate to the low temperature expected.

If the armour is made of non-corrosion-resisting material, it should be protected against corrosion by a moisture-resisting and low temperature resisting covering.

(2)   Cables installed in refrigeration spaces should not be covered by thermal insulation.

If a cable has a thermoplastic or elastomeric extruded sheath, it may be placed directly on the face of the refrigeration chamber. Care should be taken to avoid the possibility of electrolytic action if the refrigeration chamber has an aluminium facing.

11.17 Cables for special applications

(1)   Cables capable of maintaining circuit integrity under fire conditions should be used for systems which are specified as a requirement for the safety of the passengers, crew and the ship. See also 10.1(6).
Typical circuits in passenger ships for which such cables may be required include:

> fire detection alarm, gas detection alarm, CO_2 alarm;
> general alarm;
> emergency shut down circuits;
> emergency lighting.

The use of such cables may be waived subject to the approval of the Appropriate Authority providing a system is:

(i)   Self monitoring or fail safe, and / or;
(ii) Duplicated with cables run widely separated.

(2)   The types of cables permitted for service in any hazardous area are given in 23.5(3).

(3)   Where cables are operating in high ambient temperature conditions no overall recommendations can be given due to the wide span of operating temperatures possible but some guidance can be obtained by referring to BS 6141.

(4)   In general the cables specified in 10.2 and 10.3 are suitable for low temperature operating conditions with the exception that PVC insulated and sheathed cables constructed from compounds given in BS 5467, BS 6346 and IEC 502 are unsuitable for installation at temperatures lower than 0°C.
Cables manufactured in accordance with IEC 92-3 may have an outer sheath of a special grade of PVC with superior low temperature properties to those referred to in BS 6346 and IEC 502; these cables have been used for installation at temperatures of −10°C.

(5)   Cables for installation in ambient temperatures lower than −30°C have to be suitable for the environment and be able to withstand vibration at these low temperatures.

(6)   Travelling cable for electric lifts or hoists should be sheathed overall with flame-retardant compound (EM2) and should comply with BS 6977.
Where these cables are partly or wholly moving inside a hazardous area a metallic screen should be applied immediately under the outer sheath.

(7)   Where flexible cables are required for connection to portable machinery they should comply with the relevant sections of BS 6500 or BS 6007. The sheath should comply with the requirements of BS 6899 for Type RS3 sheath, or other equivalent requirements.

65

(8)   Cables for the internal wiring of switchgear should comply with BS 6231 or BS 6883.

(9)   Cables for use at radio frequencies should comply with BS 2316 and should be installed in compliance with D.4.

(10)   The type of cable to be used for special environments such as the supply to submersible pumps for water, gas and oil should be determined after consideration of the duty and the specified environments.

(11)   Cables for underwater applications should be designed to suit the specified conditions and service.

(12)   Separate cables should be used for:

(i)   Safety and emergency circuits

In order to improve overall system reliability and reduce the vulnerability of plant failure which could result from loss of a cable or signal.

(ii)   Power

Where the circuits require individual short-circuit or over current protection, except for:

(a)   Control circuit which is a branch off the main circuit. This may be carried in the same cable as the main circuit providing both the main circuit and the subsidiary are isolated by a common switch.
(b)   Where harmonic or other interference produced by thyristor equipment or similar could affect other systems equipment.

(iii)   Controls and instrumentation (both analogue and digital)

Where induced voltage or "cross talk" between circuits would cause malfunction of the system, unless separate circuits within the same cable are individually screened.

(iv)   Circuits of differing voltage bands

Circuits of differing voltage bands, as defined in Section 28, should not normally be contained in the same cable.

SECTION 12

TABLES OF
CURRENT RATING OF CABLES

These Tables apply to cables employed in the wiring of ships, but do not provide for every condition under which such cables may be used.

The current ratings are based on the maximum operating conductor temperatures as shown in Tables 12.1 to 12.19 and are applicable when up to 6 cables are bunched together. Where more than 6 cables are bunched together, a correction factor of 0.85 is to be applied, see 11.4(2). Where cables are connected in parallel the factor detailed in 11.4(6) is to be applied if necessary.

In the case of EP rubber and XLPe insulated cables the current ratings given in Tables 12.1, 12.3, 12.11 and 12.13 are based on a conductor operating temperature of 90°C and are applicable to the materials listed in Table 10.1 having that temperature classification. For these materials which have a temperature classification of 85°C a correction factor of 0.94 should be applied.

Voltage drop

The tabulated figures for voltage drop are "per metre" run, i.e. they include the voltage drop in the go and return conductors both for single-core and multicore cables.

The a.c. voltage drop values in Tables 12.1 to 12.10 and 12.19 are based on a frequency of 60 Hz. If for those sizes where reactance becomes significant, it is required to calculate voltage drop values at a frequency of 50 Hz, the following formulae will apply:

$$\text{Single-phase} \quad V_{50}^2 = 0.694 \; V_{60}^2 + 0.306 \; V_0^2$$

$$\text{Three-phase} \quad V_{50}^2 = 0.694 \; V_{60}^2 + 0.229 \; V_0^2$$

$$\text{where} \quad \begin{aligned} V_0 &= \text{d.c. volt drop per ampere per metre} \\ V_{50} &= \text{50 Hz volt drop per ampere per metre} \\ V_{60} &= \text{60 Hz volt drop per ampere per metre} \end{aligned}$$

When the d.c. volt drop is not tabulated for a 3- or 4-core cable, it can be taken as the value for a 2-core of the same conductor size.

The current ratings in the Tables are subject to the maximum permissible voltage drop not being exceeded, see 11.4(4).

Non-continuous current ratings

The non-continuous current values shown in Tables 12.11 to 12.18 have been calculated on the assumption that the intermediate periods of rest are longer than the critical duration, i.e. longer than three times the thermal time constant of the cable.

68

XLPe, EP and silicone rubber, single-core

Table 12.1 Continuous current ratings for groups of circuits (up to 6 cables bunched) for single-core XLPe, EP rubber and silicone rubber insulated cables, run open or enclosed.

XLPe and EP ambient temperature 45°C   Silicone 95°C
Conductor operating temperature 90°C   Silicone 150°C

Conductor nominal cross-sectional area	Current rating d.c. or single-phase a.c. or 3-phase a.c.	Volt drop per ampere per metre		
		d.c.	Single-phase a.c.	3-phase a.c.
1	2	3	4	5
mm²	A	mV	mV	mV
1.0	17	53	53	46
1.5	21	34	34	29
2.5	30	18	18	16
4	40	12	12	10
6	51	7.6	7.6	6.6
10	71	4.5	4.5	3.9
16	95	2.7	2.7	2.3
25	125	1.7	1.7	1.5
35	155	1.2	1.2	1.1
50	190	0.96	0.98	0.87
70	240	0.67	0.69	0.63
95	290	0.48	0.52	0.49
120	340	0.38	0.42	0.43
150	385	0.31	0.36	0.38
185	440	0.25	0.32	0.34
240	520	0.19	0.27	0.31
300	590	0.15	0.24	0.29
	d.c a.c.			
400	690 670	0.12	0.23	0.28
500	780 720	0.093	0.22	0.27
630	890 780	0.071	0.21	0.26

Rating factors

XLPe and EP RUBBER CABLES
Cooling air

temperature	35°C	40°C	45°C	50°C	55°C	60°C	65°C	70°C	75°C	80°C
Rating factor	1.11	1.05	1.00	0.94	0.88	0.82	0.75	0.67	0.58	0.47

SILICONE RUBBER CABLES
Cooling air
temperature

up to	85°C	90°C	95°C	100°C	105°C	110°C	115°C	120°C	125°C	130°C	135°C	140°C
Rating factor	1.07	1.03	1.00	0.94	0.90	0.84	0.79	0.73	0.67	0.59	0.52	0.42

Butyl rubber single-core

Table 12.2 Continuous current ratings for groups of circuits (up to 6 cables bunched) for single-core butyl rubber insulated cables, run open or enclosed.

Ambient temperature 45°C
Conductor operating temperature 80°C

Conductor nominal cross-sectional area	Current rating d.c. or single-phase a.c. or 3-phase a.c.	Volt drop per ampere per metre		
		d.c.	Single-phase a.c.	3-phase a.c.
1	2	3	4	5
mm²	A	mV	mV	mV
1.0	15	53	53	46
1.5	19	34	34	29
2.5	26	18	18	16
4	35	12	12	10
6	45	7.6	7.6	6.6
10	63	4.5	4.5	3.9
16	84	2.7	2.7	2.3
25	110	1.7	1.7	1.5
35	140	1.2	1.2	1.1
50	165	0.96	0.98	0.87
70	215	0.67	0.69	0.63
95	260	0.48	0.52	0.49
120	300	0.38	0.42	0.43
150	340	0.31	0.36	0.38
185	390	0.25	0.32	0.34
240	460	0.19	0.27	0.31
300	530	0.15	0.24	0.29
	d.c a.c.			
400	610 590	0.12	0.23	0.28
500	690 640	0.093	0.22	0.27
630	790 690	0.071	0.21	0.26

Rating factors

Cooling air temperature	35°C	40°C	45°C	50°C	55°C	60°C	65°C	70°C
Rating factor	1.13	1.07	1.00	0.93	0.85	0.76	0.65	0.53

XLPe, EP rubber twin and multicore

Table 12.3 Continuous current ratings for groups of circuits (up to 6 cables bunched) for twin and multicore XLPe, EP rubber insulated cables, run open or enclosed.

XLPe and EP ambient temperature 45°C
Conductor operating temperature   90°C

Conductor nominal cross-sectional area	Twin cables			Three- and four-core cables	
	Current rating d.c. or single-phase a.c.	Volt drop per ampere per metre		Current rating 3-phase a.c.	Volt drop per ampere per metre
		d.c.	Single-phase a.c.		
1	2	3	4	5	6
mm²	A	mV	mV	A	mV
1.0	14	54	54	12	47
1.5	18	35	35	15	30
2.5	25	18	18	21	16
4	34	12	12	29	10
6	43	7.8	7.8	36	6.7
10	60	4.6	4.6	50	4.0
16	81	2.7	2.7	67	8.3
25	105	1.7	1.7	89	1.5
35	135	1.2	1.2	105	1.1
50	165	0.98	1.0	135	0.89
70	200	0.68	0.70	170	0.64
95	250	0.49	0.53	205	0.50
120	290	0.39	0.43	240	0.44
150	330	0.31	0.36	270	0.38
185	370	0.25	0.32	305	0.34
240	445	0.19	0.27	365	0.31
300	505	0.15	0.24	415	0.29

Rating factors

Cooling air temperature	35°C	40°C	45°C	50°C	55°C	60°C	65°C	70°C	75°C	80°C
Rating factor	1.11	1.05	1.00	0.94	0.88	0.82	0.75	0.67	0.58	0.47

Butyl rubber twin and multicore

Table 12.4 Continuous current ratings for groups of circuits (up to 6 cables bunched) for twin and multicore butyl rubber insulated cables, run open or enclosed.

Ambient temperature 45°C
Conductor operating temperature 80°C

Conductor nominal cross-sectional area	Twin cables			Three- and four-core cables	
	Current rating d.c. or single-phase a.c.	Volt drop per ampere per metre		Current rating 3-phase a.c.	Volt drop per ampere per metre
		d.c.	Single-phase a.c.		
1	2	3	4	5	6
mm²	A	mV	mV	A	mV
1.0	13	54	54	11	47
1.5	16	35	35	13	30
2.5	22	18	18	18	16
4	30	12	12	25	10
6	38	7.8	7.8	32	6.7
10	54	4.6	4.6	44	4.0
16	71	2.7	2.7	59	2.3
25	94	1.7	1.7	77	1.5
35	120	1.2	1.2	98	1.1
50	140	0.98	1.0	115	0.89
70	185	0.68	0.70	150	0.64
95	220	0.49	0.53	180	0.50
120	255	0.39	0.43	210	0.44
150	290	0.31	0.36	240	0.38
185	330	0.25	0.32	275	0.34
240	390	0.19	0.27	320	0.31
300	450	0.15	0.24	370	0.29

Rating factors

Cooling air temperature	35°C	40°C	45°C	50°C	55°C	60°C	65°C	70°C
Rating factor	1.13	1.07	1.00	0.93	0.85	0.76	0.65	0.53

PVC single-core

Table 12.5 Continuous current ratings for groups of circuits (up to 6 cables bunched) for single-core IEC 92-351 Type PVC/A insulated cables, run open or enclosed.

Ambient temperature 45°C
Conductor operating temperature 60°C

Conductor nominal cross-sectional area 1	Current rating d.c. or single-phase a.c. or 3-phase a.c. 2	Volt drop per ampere per metre		
		d.c. 3	Single-phase a.c. 4	3-phase a.c. 5
mm²	A	mV	mV	mV
1.0	8	53	40	35
1.5	12	27	27	23
2.5	17	16	16	14
4	22	10	10	8.8
6	29	6.8	6.8	5.9
10	40	4.0	4.0	3.5
16	54	2.6	2.6	2.2
25	71	1.6	1.6	1.4
35	87	1.2	1.2	1.0
50	105	0.91	0.94	0.83
70	135	0.63	0.66	0.61
95	165	0.45	0.48	0.47
120	190	0.36	0.42	0.41
150	220	0.29	0.36	0.37
185	250	0.24	0.31	0.33
240	290	0.18	0.26	0.31
300	335	0.14	0.25	0.29
	d.c a.c.			
400	390 380	0.12	0.23	0.28
500	450 430	0.086	0.21	0.27
630	520 470	0.068	0.20	0.26

Rating factors

Cooling air temperature	35°C	40°C	45°C	50°C
Rating factor	1.29	1.15	1.00	0.82

PVC single-core

Table 12.6 Continuous current ratings for groups of circuits (up to 6 cables bunched) for single-core BS 6746 Type TI1 PVC insulated cables, run open or enclosed.

Ambient temperature 45°C
Conductor operating temperature 70°C

Conductor nominal cross-sectional area 1	Current rating d.c. or single-phase a.c. or 3-phase a.c. 2	Volt drop per ampere per metre		
		d.c. 3	Single-phase a.c. 4	3-phase a.c. 5
mm²	A	mV	mV	mV
1.0	10	44	44	38
1.5	15	29	29	25
2.5	22	18	18	15
4	28	11	11	9.5
6	37	7.3	7.3	6.4
10	52	4.4	4.4	3.8
16	70	2.8	2.8	2.4
25	92	1.75	1.75	1.5
35	110	1.25	1.25	1.1
50	135	0.93	0.95	0.82
70	175	0.63	0.66	0.57
95	215	0.46	0.50	0.43
120	245	0.36	0.41	0.36
150	285	0.29	0.34	0.30
185	325	0.23	0.29	0.26
240	375	0.18	0.25	0.22
300	430	0.145	0.22	0.19
	d.c a.c.			
400	500 490	0.105	0.20	0.175
500	580 550	0.086	0.185	0.16
630	670 610	0.068	0.175	0.15

Rating factors

Cooling air temperature	35°C	40°C	45°C	50°C	55°C	60°C
Rating factor	1.18	1.10	1.00	0.89	0.77	0.63

PVC twin and multicore

Table 12.7 **Continuous current ratings for groups of circuits (up to 6 cables bunched) for twin and multicore IEC 92-351 Type PVC/A insulated cables, run open or enclosed.**

Ambient temperature 45°C
Conductor operating temperature 60°C

Conductor nominal cross-sectional area	Twin cables				Three- and four-core cables	
	Current rating d.c. or single-phase a.c.	Volt drop per ampere per metre			Current rating 3-phase a.c.	Volt drop per ampere per metre
			d.c.	Single-phase a.c.		
1	2	3		4	5	6
mm²	A	mV		mV	A	mV
1.0	7	41		41	6	35
1.5	10	28		28	8	24
2.5	14	17		17	12	15
4	19	11		11	15	9.1
6	25	7		7	20	6
10	34	4.1		4.1	28	3.6
16	46	2.6		2.6	38	2.2
25	61	1.7		1.7	50	1.5
35	74	1.2		1.2	61	1.0
50	89	0.93		0.94	74	0.82
70	115	0.64		0.67	95	0.58
95	140	0.46		0.50	115	0.43
120	160	0.37		0.41	135	0.35
150	185	0.30		0.34	155	0.30
185	210	0.24		0.30	175	0.25
240	245	0.19		0.26	205	0.22
300	285	0.15		0.23	235	0.20
	d.c 330 a.c 320	0.12		0.21	d.c. 275 a.c 265	0.18
400						

		Rating factors			
Cooling air temperature		35°C	40°C	45°C	50°C
Rating factor		1.29	1.15	1.00	0.82

75

PVC twin and multicore

Table 12.8 Continuous current ratings for groups of circuits (up to 6 cables bunched) for twin and multicore BS 6746 Type TI1 PVC insulated cables, run open or enclosed.

Ambient temperature 45°C
Conductor operating temperature 70°C

Conductor nominal cross-sectional area	Twin cables			Three- and four-core cables	
	Current rating d.c. or single-phase a.c.	Volt drop per ampere per metre		Current rating 3-phase a.c.	Volt drop per ampere per metre
		d.c.	Single-phase a.c.		
1	2	3	4	5	6
mm²	A	mV	mV	A	mV
1.0	9	44	44	8	38
1.5	13	29	29	10	25
2.5	18	18	18	15	15
4	25	11	11	19	9.5
6	32	7.3	7.3	26	6.4
10	44	4.4	4.4	36	3.8
16	59	2.8	2.8	49	2.4
25	79	1.75	1.75	65	1.5
35	95	1.25	1.25	79	1.10
50	115	0.93	0.94	95	0.81
70	150	0.63	0.65	125	0.57
95	180	0.46	0.50	150	0.43
120	205	0.36	0.41	175	0.35
150	240	0.29	0.34	200	0.29
185	270	0.23	0.29	225	0.25
240	315	0.18	0.24	265	0.21
300	370	0.145	0.21	305	0.185
	d.c 425 a.c 415	0.105	0.185	d.c. 355 a.c 340	0.160
400					

Rating factors

Cooling air temperature	35°C	40°C	45°C	50°C	55°C	60°C
Rating factor	1.18	1.10	1.00	0.89	0.77	0.63

Mineral, sheath bare, not exposed to touch, single, twin and multicore

Table 12.9 Continuous current ratings for groups of circuits (up to 6 cables bunched) for single, twin and multicore light and heavy duty mineral insulated metal sheathed cables having the sheath bare and not exposed to touch and not in contact with combustible materials.

Ambient temperature 45°C for termination operating temperature 105°C
Ambient temperature 90°C for termination operating temperature 150°C

Conductor nominal cross-sectional area	Single-core cables				Twin cables			Three- or four-core cables	
	Current rating d.c. or single-phase a.c. or 3-phase a.c.	Volt drop per ampere per metre			Current rating d.c. or single-phase a.c.	Volt drop per ampere per metre		Current rating 3-phase a.c.	Volt drop per ampere per metre 3-phase
		d.c.	Single-phase a.c.	3-phase a.c.		d.c.	Single-phase a.c.		
1	2	3	4	5	6	7	8	9	10
mm^2	A	mV	mV	mV	A	mV	mV	A	mV
1.0	19	47	47	40	23	47	47	19	40
1.5	25	31	31	27	29	31	31	25	27
2.5	33	19	19	16	40	19	19	33	16
4	44	12	12	10	53	12	12	43	10
6	56	7.8	7.8	6.8	67	7.8	7.8	55	6.8
10	77	4.7	4.7	4.1	92	4.7	4.7	75	4.1
16	101	3.0	3.0	2.6	121	3.0	3.0	99	2.6
25	132	1.85	1.85	1.65	158	1.85	1.85	128	1.65
35	162	1.35	1.35	1.20	—	—	—	—	—
50	201	1.00	1.00	0.88	—	—	—	—	—
70	246	0.69	0.71	0.62	—	—	—	—	—
95	295	0.51	0.54	0.47	—	—	—	—	—
120	339	0.41	0.44	0.38	—	—	—	—	—
150	388	0.33	0.36	0.32	—	—	—	—	—
185	440	0.27	0.31	0.27	—	—	—	—	—
240	513	0.21	0.26	0.22	—	—	—	—	—

The tabulated volt drop values are for cables operating at 105°C
For cables operating at 150°C the tabulated values of volt drop should be multiplied by 1.18

Rating factors

	25°C	35°C	45°C	55°C	65°C	75°C	85°C	95°C	105°C	115°C	125°C	135°C	145°C
For cables with 105°C terminations	1.16	1.06	1.00	0.91	0.80	0.68	0.53	0.36	—	—	—	—	—
For cables with 150°C terminations	1.27	1.24	1.19	1.15	1.10	1.06	1.01	0.95	0.91	0.81	0.67	0.50	0.27

Mineral, PVC covered, exposed to touch, single, twin and multicore

Table 12.10 Continuous current ratings for groups of circuits (up to 6 cables bunched) for single, twin and multicore light and heavy duty mineral insulated metal sheathed cables exposed to touch or having an overall covering of PVC.

Ambient temperature 45°C
Conductor operating temperature 70°C

Conductor nominal cross-sectional area	Single-core cables				Twin cables			Three- or four-core cables	
	Current rating d.c. or single-phase a.c. or 3-phase a.c.	Volt drop per ampere per metre			Current rating d.c. or single-phase a.c.	Volt drop per ampere per metre		Current rating 3-phase a.c.	Volt drop per ampere per metre 3-phase
		d.c.	Single-phase a.c.	3-phase a.c.		d.c.	Single-phase a.c.		
1	2	3	4	5	6	7	8	9	10
mm²	A	mV	mV	mV	A	mV	mV	mV	A
1.0	12	42	42	36	13	42	42	11	36
1.5	15	28	28	24	16	28	28	13	24
2.5	20	17	17	14	22	17	17	18	14
4	27	10	10	9.1	28	10	10	24	9.1
6	34	7	7	6.0	36	7.2	7.2	31	6.0
10	46	4.2	4.2	3.6	49	4.2	4.2	41	3.6
16	62	2.6	2.6	2.3	65	2.6	2.6	53	2.3
25	80	1.65	1.65	1.45	85	1.65	1.65	70	1.45
35	98	1.20	1.20	1.10	—	—	—	—	—
50	122	0.89	0.91	0.80	—	—	—	—	—
70	149	0.62	0.64	0.56	—	—	—	—	—
95	179	0.46	0.49	0.43	—	—	—	—	—
120	206	0.37	0.41	0.36	—	—	—	—	—
150	236	0.30	0.34	0.30	—	—	—	—	—
185	267	0.25	0.29	0.26	—	—	—	—	—
240	312	0.19	0.25	0.22	—	—	—	—	—

Rating factors

Cooling air temperature	25°C	30°C	35°C	40°C	45°C	50°C	55°C	60°C
Rating factor	1.34	1.30	1.21	1.10	1.00	0.87	0.74	0.58

Ratings for non-continuous service

XLPe and EP rubber without metal sheath or armour, single, twin and multicore

Table 12.11   Current ratings for non-continuously loaded single, twin and multicore XLPe and EP rubber insulated cables without metal sheath and/or armour.

NOTE: The non-continuous ratings for conductor sizes up to and including 35 mm^2 are the same as the continuous ratings (see Tables 12.1 and 12.3)

Ambient temperature 45°C
Conductor operating temperature 90°C

Conductor nominal cross-sectional area	Single-core cables		Twin cables		Three- and four-core cables	
	d.c. or single-phase a.c. or 3-phase a.c.		d.c. or single-phase a.c.		3-phase a.c.	
	Half hour rating	One hour rating	Half hour rating	One hour rating	Half hour rating	One hour rating
1	2	3	4	5	6	7
mm^2	A	A	A	A	A	A
50	205	200	185	175	155	145
70	260	255	235	215	205	185
95	330	305	295	280	265	230
120	385	360	355	315	315	270
150	450	420	415	365	370	315
185	530	475	495	425	440	365
240	650	570	610	510	550	450
300	760	670	730	600	660	525
	d.c a.c.	d.c. a.c.				
400	930 900	900 770	—	—	—	—
500	1100 1010	920 850	—	—	—	—
630	1290 1140	1080 950	—	—	—	—

Rating factors

Cooling air temperature	35°C	40°C	45°C	50°C	55°C	60°C	65°C	70°C	75°C	80°C
Rating factor	1.11	1.05	1.00	0.94	0.88	0.82	0.75	0.67	0.58	0.47

Ratings for non-continuous service

Butyl rubber without metal sheath or armour single, twin and multicore

Table 12.12 Current ratings for non-continuously loaded single, twin and multicore butyl rubber insulated cables without metal sheath and/or armour.

NOTE: The non-continuous ratings for conductor sizes up to and including 35 mm^2 are the same as the continuous ratings (see Tables 12.2 and 12.4)

Ambient temperature 45°C
Conductor operating temperature 80°C

Conductor nominal cross-sectional area	Single-core cables		Twin cables		Three- and four-core cables	
	d.c. or single-phase a.c. or 3-phase a.c.		d.c. or single-phase a.c.		3-phase a.c.	
	Half hour rating	One hour rating	Half hour rating	One hour rating	Half hour rating	One hour rating
1	2	3	4	5	6	7
mm^2	A	A	A	A	A	A
50	175	175	155	150	135	125
70	235	230	215	200	185	165
95	290	275	265	240	230	200
120	340	320	315	280	275	235
150	400	365	370	325	330	280
185	470	425	440	375	395	325
240	570	510	540	455	480	395
300	680	590	650	540	580	470
	d.c a.c.	d.c. a.c.				
400	820 800	700 680	—	—	—	—
500	970 900	810 760	—	—	—	—
630	1150 1010	960 840	—	—	—	—

Rating factors

Cooling air temperature	35°C	40°C	45°C	50°C	55°C	60°C	65°C	70°C
Rating factor	1.13	1.07	1.00	0.93	0.85	0.76	0.65	0.53

Ratings for non-continuous service

XLPe and EP rubber with metal sheath and/or armour, single, twin and multicore

Table 12.13   Current ratings for non-continuously loaded single, twin and multicore XLPe and EP rubber insulated cables with metal sheath and/or armour.

> **NOTE:** The non-continuous ratings for conductor sizes up to and including 6 mm² are the same as the continuous ratings (see Tables 12.1 and 12.3)

Ambient temperature 45°C
Conductor operating temperature 90°C

Conductor nominal cross-sectional area	Single-core cables				Twin cables		Three- and four-core cables	
	d.c. or single-phase a.c. or 3-phase a.c.				d.c. or single-phase a.c.		3-phase a.c.	
	Half hour rating		One hour rating		Half hour rating	One hour rating	Half hour rating	One hour rating
1	2		3		4	5	6	7
mm²	A		A		A	A	A	A
10	75		75		67	64	56	53
16	105		100		91	86	77	71
25	145		135		120	115	105	98
35	175		165		160	145	135	115
50	225		205		205	180	175	155
70	285		260		265	230	235	195
95	365		325		340	290	300	250
120	440		380		405	340	360	285
150	510		440		480	400	425	340
185	600		500		540	455	500	400
240	730		610		700	550	620	490
300	870		720		835	660	740	570
	d.c	a.c.	d.c.	a.c.				
400	1050	1020	860	830	—	—	—	—
500	1250	1140	1000	910	—	—	—	—
630	1470	1300	1170	1030	—	—	—	—

Rating factors

Cooling air temperature	35°C	40°C	45°C	50°C	55°C	60°C	65°C	70°C	75°C	80°C
Rating factor	1.11	1.05	1.00	0.94	0.88	0.82	0.75	0.67	0.58	0.47

Ratings for non-continuous service

Butyl cables with metal sheath and/or armour, single, twin and multicore

Table 12.14 Current ratings for non-continuously loaded single, twin and multicore butyl rubber insulated cables with metal sheath and/or armour.

NOTE: The non-continuous ratings for conductor sizes up to and including 6 mm^2 are the same as the continuous ratings (see Tables 12.2 and 12.4)

Ambient temperature 45°C
Conductor operating temperature 80°C

Conductor nominal cross-sectional area	Single-core cables		Twin cables		Three- and four-core cables	
	d.c. or single-phase a.c. or 3-phase a.c.		d.c. or single-phase a.c.		3-phase a.c.	
1	Half hour rating 2	One hour rating 3	Half hour rating 4	One hour rating 5	Half hour rating 6	One hour rating 7
mm^2	A	A	A	A	A	A
10	67	67	59	57	49	47
16	92	89	80	76	68	63
25	120	115	110	100	93	84
35	160	150	145	130	125	110
50	195	180	175	155	150	130
70	260	235	240	210	205	175
95	325	290	300	255	260	215
120	385	335	360	300	315	260
150	450	390	425	350	375	300
185	530	445	500	405	445	355
240	650	540	620	490	550	425
300	770	640	750	590	710	530
	d.c a.c.	d.c. a.c.				
400	930 840	760 730	—	—	—	—
500	1100 1020	880 810	—	—	—	—
630	1310 1140	1030 900	—	—	—	—

Rating factors

Cooling air temperature	35°C	40°C	45°C	50°C	55°C	60°C	65°C	70°C
Rating factor	1.13	1.07	1.00	0.93	0.85	0.76	0.65	0.53

PVC without metal sheath or armour, single, twin and multicore

Table 12.15 Current ratings for non-continously loaded single, twin and multicore IEC 92-351 Type PVC/A insulated cables without metal sheath or armour.

NOTE: The non-continuous ratings for conductor sizes up to and including 35 mm^2 are the same as the continuous ratings (see Tables 12.5 and 12.7)

Ambient temperature 45°C
Conductor operating temperature 60°C

Conductor nominal cross-sectional area	Single-core cables		Twin cables		Three- and four-core cables	
	d.c. or single-phase a.c. or 3-phase a.c.		d.c. or single-phase a.c.		3-phase a.c.	
	Half hour rating	One hour rating	Half hour rating	One hour rating	Half hour rating	One hour rating
1	2	3	4	5	6	7
mm^2	A	A	A	A	A	A
50	110	110	100	94	87	80
70	145	145	135	125	115	105
95	185	175	170	155	145	130
120	215	205	200	175	180	155
150	255	240	235	205	210	180
185	300	270	280	240	250	210
240	360	320	340	285	310	250
300	430	375	415	340	370	300
	d.c a.c.	d.c. a.c.	d.c. a.c	d.c. a.c.	d.c. a.c.	d.c. a.c.
400	530 510	450 435	510 495	410 400	460 445	365 350
500	630 600	530 510	— —	— —	— —	— —
630	760 690	630 570	— —	— —	— —	— —

Cooling air temperature	35°C	40°C	45°C	50°C
Rating factor	1.29	1.15	1.00	0.82

Ratings for non-continuous service

PVC without metal sheath or armour, single, twin and multicore

Table 12.16 Current ratings for non-continuously loaded single, twin and multicore IEC 92-351 Type PVC/A insulated cables with metal sheath and/or armour.

NOTE: The non-continuous ratings for conductor sizes up to and including 6 mm^2 are the same as the continuous ratings (see Tables 12.5 and 12.7)

Ambient temperature 45°C
Conductor operating temperature 60°C

Conductor nominal cross-sectional area	Single-core cables		Twin cables		Three- and four-core cables	
	d.c. or single-phase a.c. or 3-phase a.c.		d.c. or single-phase a.c.		3-phase a.c.	
	Half hour rating	One hour rating	Half hour rating	One hour rating	Half hour rating	One hour rating
1	2	3	4	5	6	7
mm^2	A	A	A	A	A	A
10	43	42	37	36	31	30
16	59	57	52	49	44	41
25	79	75	71	66	61	55
35	99	93	90	81	77	68
50	125	115	110	99	98	84
70	165	145	150	130	130	110
95	205	180	190	160	165	140
120	245	215	225	190	205	165
150	290	250	270	225	240	195
185	340	285	315	260	285	225
240	410	340	390	310	350	275
300	490	405	475	370	425	325
	d.c 590 / a.c. 580	d.c. 485 / a.c. 470	d.c. 580 / a.c 560	d.c. 445 / a.c. 430	d.c. 530 / a.c. 510	d.c. 395 / a.c. 380
400						
500	720 / 680	570 / 550	— / —	— / —	— / —	— / —
630	860 / 780	680 / 620	— / —	— / —	— / —	— / —

Cooling air temperature 35°C 40°C 45°C 50°C
Rating factor   1.29 1.15 1.00 0.82

Ratings for non-continuous service

PVC without metal sheath or armour, single, twin and multicore

Table 12.17 Current ratings for non-continuously loaded single, twin and multicore BS 6746 Type TI1 PVC insulated cables without metal sheath or armour.

NOTE: The non-continuous ratings for conductor sizes up to and including 35 mm^2 are the same as the continuous ratings (see Tables 12.6 and 12.8)

Ambient temperature 45°C
Conductor operating temperature 70°C

Conductor nominal cross-sectional area	Single-core cables		Twin cables		Three- and four-core cables	
	d.c. or single-phase a.c. or 3-phase a.c.		d.c. or single-phase a.c.		3-phase a.c.	
	Half hour rating	One hour rating	Half hour rating	One hour rating	Half hour rating	One hour rating
1	2	3	4	5	6	7
mm^2	A	A	A	A	A	A
50	140	140	130	120	110	105
70	185	185	175	160	150	135
95	240	225	220	200	185	170
120	275	265	260	225	230	200
150	330	310	305	265	270	230
185	385	350	360	310	325	270
240	465	415	440	370	400	325
300	550	485	540	440	475	390
	d.c a.c.	d.c. a.c.	d.c. a.c	d.c. a.c.	d.c. a.c.	d.c. a.c.
400	680 660	580 560	650 640	530 520	600 570	470 450
500	810 770	680 660	— —	— —	— —	— —
630	980 890	815 740	— —	— —	— —	— —

Cooling air temperature	35°C	40°C	45°C	50°C	55°C	60°C
Rating factor	1.18	1.10	1.00	0.89	0.77	0.63

Ratings for non-continuous service

PVC cables with metal sheath and/or armour, single, twin and multicore

Table 12.18   Current ratings for non-continuously loaded single, twin and multicore BS 6746 Type TI1 PVC insulated cables with metal sheath and/or armour.

NOTE: The non-continuous ratings for conductor sizes up to and including 6 mm^2 are the same as the continuous ratings (see Tables 12.6 and 12.8)

Ambient temperature 45°C
Conductor operating temperature 70°C

Conductor nominal cross-sectional area	Single-core cables		Twin cables		Three- and four-core cables	
	d.c. or single-phase a.c. or 3-phase a.c.		d.c. or single-phase a.c.		3-phase a.c.	
	Half hour rating	One hour rating	Half hour rating	One hour rating	Half hour rating	One hour rating
1	2	3	4	5	6	7
mm^2	A	A	A	A	A	A
10	55	54	48	46	40	39
16	76	74	67	63	57	53
25	100	97	92	85	79	71
35	130	120	115	105	99	88
50	160	150	140	130	125	110
70	215	185	195	170	170	140
95	265	230	245	205	215	180
120	315	275	290	245	265	215
150	375	325	350	290	310	250
185	440	370	405	335	370	290
240	530	440	500	400	450	355
300	630	520	610	475	550	420
	d.c a.c.	d.c. a.c.	d.c. a.c	d.c. a.c.	d.c. a.c.	d.c. a.c.
400	760 750	630 610	750 720	570 550	580 660	510 490
500	930 880	740 710	— —	— —	— —	— —
630	1100 1010	880 800	— —	— —	— —	— —

Cooling air temperature	35°C	40°C	45°C	50°C	55°C	60°C
Rating factor	1.18	1.10	1.00	0.89	0.77	0.63

Table 12.19   **Continuous current ratings for flexible cords insulated with 60°C rubber, PVC, 85°C rubber, 150°C rubber or glass fibre to BS 6500.**

Nominal cross-sectional area of conductor	Current rating d.c. or single-phase a.c. or 3-phase a.c.	Volt drop per ampere per metre*	
		d.c. or single-phase a.c.	3-phase a.c.
1	2	3	4
mm^2	A	mV	mV
0.5	3	93	80
0.75	6	62	54
1.0	10	46	40
1.25	13	37	32
1.5	16	32	27
	d.c. or single-phase a.c / 3-phase a.c.		
2.5	25 20	19	16
4	32 25	12	10

Rating factors

60°C rubber and PVC cords

Cooling air temperature	35°C	40°C	45°C	50°C	55°C	
Rating factor	0.92	0.82	0.71	0.58	0.41	

85°C rubber cords having a HOFR sheath or a heat resisting PVC sheath

Cooling air temperature	35°C to 50°C	55°C	60°C	65°C	70°C	
Rating factor	1.0	0.96	0.83	0.67	0.47	

150°C rubber cords

Cooling air temperature	35°C to 120°C	125°C	130°C	135°C	140°C	145°C
Rating factor	1.0	0.96	0.85	0.74	0.60	0.42

Glass fibre cords

Cooling air temperature	35°C to 150°C	155°C	160°C	165°C	170°C	175°C
Rating factor	1.0	0.92	0.82	0.71	0.57	0.40

* NOTE: The tabulated values above are for 60°C rubber insulated and PVC-insulated flexible cords and for other types of flexible cords they are to be multiplied by the following factors: For 85°C rubber insulated 1.085; 150°C rubber insulated 1.306; 185°C glass fibre 1.425.

SECTION 13

MOTOR CONTROL GEAR

13.1 Construction and temperature limits

The construction, rating and testing of control gear should be in accordance with BS 587, BS 775, BS 4941, BS 5227, BS 5424, BS 5486, BS 5856, BS 6141, BS 6195 or BS 6231, as applicable.

13.2 Glazed windows of enclosing cases should be as small as practicable, consistent with their purpose, and suitable protection should be arranged, where necessary, against accidental breakage.

13.3 Every electric motor should be provided with efficient means of starting and stopping, the latter so placed as to be easily operated by the person controlling the motor. This requirement may be relaxed in special circumstances for motors having a rating of 0.5 kW or less.

(1) Means should be provided to prevent automatic re-starting after a stoppage due to a drop in voltage, or complete failure of supply, where unexpected re-starting of the motor might be undesirable.

NOTE 1 This requirement may be relaxed in special circumstances, e.g. where it is admissible to arrange for the starting of a motor at irregular intervals in response to an automatic control device or where a dangerous condition might result from the failure of a motor to start after a temporary interruption of the supply, for example, a steering gear motor.

NOTE 2 A single device may serve to prevent automatic re-starting of a group of motors.

(2) Means of isolation should be provided suitably placed and so connected that all voltage may thereby be cut from the motor and all apparatus including any automatic circuit-breaker used therewith.

NOTE 1 A single means of isolation may be provided for a group of motors and associated control apparatus where, for the purpose of carrying out inspection or other work on any individual motor in the group or on the control apparatus directly associated with such a motor, simultaneous isolation of the whole group is acceptable.

NOTE 2 The means of isolation referred to in 13.3(2) may be the fuses in each live pole or phase, provided they are so arranged so that they can be readily and safely removed and retained by persons authorised to have access to the motor and associated apparatus. Where small appliances may be safely isolated by a plug and socket arrangement, additional means are not necessary.

(3)   Where necessary for safety, local stopping facilities should be provided.

13.4   Where a single master-starter system (i.e. a starter used for controlling a number of motors successively) is used, the apparatus should provide undervoltage and overcurrent protection and means of isolation for each motor not less effective than required for systems using a separate starter for each motor. Where the starter is of the automatic type, suitable alternative or emergency means should be provided for manual operation. Where motors are provided for duplicated services, the starting portion should be duplicated and means should be provided for the standby unit to be put into immediate operation in the event of failure of one of the starters.

13.5   Emergency stop controls for motor-driven fuel-oil transfer and fuel-oil pressure pumps should be provided at a readily accessible point outside the compartments in which the pumps are situated. The controls should be of the manual re-set type and suitably labelled.

13.6   All power ventilation,except machinery and cargo space ventilation and any alternative ventilation specially provided for control stations outside the machinery spaces, should be fitted with controls so grouped that any fans may be stopped from either of two separate positions which should be situated as far apart as practicable. Controls provided for the power ventilation serving machinery spaces should also be grouped so as to be operable from two positions, one of which should be outside such spaces. Fans serving power ventilation systems to cargo spaces should be capable of being stopped from a safe position outside such spaces. Controls should be of the manual re-set type and suitably labelled.

Exemption: This recommendation does not apply to small fans connected to lighting circuits.

13.7   Motor-driven pumps designed to discharge above the water line in the way of lifeboat launching should be provided with emergency stop controls installed in locked boxes having breakable covers, e.g. glass, conveniently located. The controls should be of the manual re-set type and suitably labelled.

13.8   Lifts

(1)   Lift electrical equipment should comply with the appropriate requirements of BS 5655.

(2)   Lifts, other than those used exclusively for goods, should be arranged so that in the event of failure of the main supply, they will deck automatically

using the emergency supply and should then allow the gates to be opened, or should be provided with other satisfactory means for escape of occupants.

NOTE: Unless the emergency generator is arranged to start automatically on mains failure the emergency supply should be taken to include the half-hour transitional battery, when fitted.

(3)   One lamp in each lift and the alarm facility should be supplied from an emergency power source.

13.9   Magnetic brakes

(1)   Series-wound and compound-wound brakes should release on first-step starting current of the motor. Series-wound brakes should hold off under all working conditions including light running. Equipment that provides electric controlled lowering should be fitted with compound-wound or shunt-wound brakes. If compound-wound, the regenerative current passing through the series coil should not allow the brake to operate. Shunt brake coils should be so constructed or protected that they are guarded against damage to their windings by inductive discharge. A series resistor and / or discharge resistor may be used.

(2)   The temperature rise of coils when tested in accordance with the brake rating should not exceed that permitted on motors with which they are being used. Where the coils are in close proximity to the lining, the brakes should be tested under conditions such that any heat transmitted from the friction surfaces is taken into account. Where the motor with which the brake is being used can run light for periods in excess of the time of its full-load rating, the brake coils should correspond to the light running period.

13.10   Magnetic clutches

The recommendations made in 13. 9 for shunt-wound brakes apply generally to magnetic clutches. When the coil is energised, the clutch should take up the drive smoothly and positively. No end-thrust should be exerted from the clutch, the pressure between members being balanced within the clutch itself. Magnetic clutches should be balanced. Suitable means for taking up wear of the linings should be provided. Collector rings for current supply to the clutch should be of non-corrodible material. Double brush-contacts should, preferably, be fitted to provide positive contact.

90

SECTION 14

BATTERIES

General

14.1   This Section relates to secondary batteries of the vented and sealed type which are installed permanently in position.

14.2   A vented battery is one in which the products of electrolysis can be replaced and which may release gas whilst operating on charge and overcharge.

14.3   A sealed type battery is one in which the products of electrolysis cannot be replaced and is capable of operating on charge, overcharge and discharge without releasing gas under normal conditions but which allows the escape of gas if the internal pressure exceeds a critical value.

14.4   Each battery should be provided with a durable name-plate securely attached or, alternatively, fitted adjacent to the battery, bearing the maker's name and type designation, the ampere/hour rating at some specific rate of discharge (preferably that corresponding to the duty for the specific application) and, for lead-acid batteries, the specific gravity of the electrolyte when the battery is fully charged.

14.5   The batteries should be arranged to facilitate ease of installation, replacement and where necessary, maintenance.

14.6   The battery may consist of single cells assembled in crates or trays or upon a stand or stands of wood or other suitable material. Crates or trays should be provided with means to facilitate handling and should preferably not exceed 100 kg in weight. Where metal stands are used, non-absorbent insulation appropriate to the working voltage should be provided between the cells and stands. Similar insulating materials should be employed to restrict movement of the cells arising from the motion of the ship. In addition, metallic stands should be insulated from the structure where the battery has a nominal working voltage exceeding 120 volts.

14.7   All fittings should be non-corrodible or should be treated with electrolyte resistant material.

14.8   Batteries should be located where they are not exposed to excessive heat, extreme cold, spray or other conditions which would impair performance or accelerate deterioration.

NOTE: The best operating conditions for a battery are obtained when the ambient temperature is within the range 15°C to 25°C.

91

Attention is drawn to the susceptibility of battery performance in the ambient conditions described in 1.10 against which the battery systems should be designed.

Vented Type Batteries

14.9   Construction

The cells of all batteries should be so constructed as to prevent spilling of the electrolyte due to inclination of 40° from normal during handling. The plates should be so arranged that they are firmly secured against motion within the containers and should be designed for the least practical shedding of active material. The design should also minimise the emission of electrolyte spray.

14.10   Installation

(1)   Where acid is used as the electrolyte, a tray of lead or wood lined with lead or other electrolyte resisting material should be provided below the cells to contain the electrolyte without leaking. The lining should be water-tight and carried up to not less than 75 mm on all sides. If of lead, the lining should be 1.5 mm minimum thickness.

(2)   Alternatively, the deck below the cells should be protected with lead or other acid resisting materials to minimise risk of any acid lodging in contact with the structure of the ship. The lining should span the entire floor and be carried up to not less than 150 mm on all sides.

(3)   For alkaline batteries similar arrangements should be adopted using a lining of electrolyte resisting material. If the lining is of steel it should be not less than 0.8 mm thickness. Deck boxes should be lined to a depth of 75 mm consistent with the methods described above. The interiors of all battery compartments including crates, trays, boxes, shelves and other structural parts therein should be painted with corrosion-resistant paint. Materials used for coating and lining should not be likely to emit vapours detrimental to the batteries.

(4)   A permanent notice should be exhibited prohibiting naked lights and smoking in battery compartments.

14.11   Location

(1)   Batteries connected to a charging device with a power output of more than 2 kW (calculated from the maximum obtainable charging current and the nominal voltage of the battery) should be installed in a compartment assigned to batteries only, but may be installed in a suitable box on deck.

(2)   Batteries connected to a charging device with a power output within the range 0.2 kW to 2 kW (calculated as under 14.11(1)) may be installed in accordance with one of the following alternatives:

(i) in a battery compartment;
(ii) in a box on deck;
(iii) in a box in a machinery or similar space.

(3)   Batteries connected to a charging device with a power output of less than 0.2 kW (calculated as under 14.11(1)) may be installed in accordance with one of the following alternatives:

(i) open, if protected from falling objects;
(ii) in a battery box in any suitable space.

(4)   Batteries should not be installed in sleeping quarters.

(5)   Batteries should be so located that adjacent equipment is not rendered inoperative by corrosion from battery emissions.

(6)   Starter batteries should be located as close as practicable to the engine or engines served to limit voltage drop in cables at the high current required.

(7)   No battery compartment should form a means of access to any other compartment.

(8)   Where lead acid and alkaline batteries are installed, precautions should be taken to prevent possible contamination of the electrolytes. If the same compartment is used for both battery types, separation should be provided by screens.

NOTE: Separate tools such as hydrometers, topping-up devices, etc., should be provided.

(9)   Battery compartments should have gas-tight boundaries where they adjoin accommodation or service spaces and, it is preferable, that they should be arranged with access from the open deck.

14.12   Ventilation

(1)   All compartments and boxes for storage batteries should be arranged and / or ventilated to avoid accumulation of flammable gas. Particular attention should be given to the fact that the gas evolved is lighter than air and will tend to accumulate in any pockets at the top of the space. When batteries are arranged in two or more tiers, all shelves except the lowest should have not less than 50 mm space front and back for circulation of air.

(2)   Natural ventilation for battery compartments may be employed if ducts can be run directly from the top of the compartment to the open air above, with no part of the duct more than 45° from the vertical. These ducts should not contain appliances, e. g. flame-barrier, which may impede the free passage of air or gas mixtures. If natural ventilation is impracticable or insufficient, mechanical exhaust ventilation should be provided with the

exhaust at the top of the compartment. Adequate openings, whether connected to ducts or not, for inlet air should be provided near the floor of battery compartments or boxes.

(3)   The ventilation system for battery boxes and compartments should be separate from other ventilation systems and the ducts should lead to a location in the open air where any gases can be safely diluted. The location should be away from possible sources of ignition and openings to spaces in which gases might accumulate.

(4)   In every case the ventilation arrangements should be such that the quantity of air expelled is at least equal to:

$$Q = 110 \times I \times n$$

Where Q = Quantity of air expelled in litres per hour.
      I = The maximum current delivered by the charging equipment during gas formation, but not less than $\frac{1}{4}$ of the maximum obtainable charging current in amperes.
      n = Number of cells in series.

(5)   Batteries in compartments or boxes connected to a charging device with a maximum power output of more than 2 kW should be ventilated by mechanical exhaust.

(6)   Where boxes are provided for batteries in machinery spaces and other well-ventilated compartments, the duct should terminate not less than 900 mm above the battery enclosure.

(7)   Boxes for batteries should have, for ventilation, openings near the top to permit escape of gas. Holes for air inlet should be provided on at least two opposite sides of the box. The entire box, including openings for ventilation, should be sufficiently weatherproof to prevent entrance of spray or rain.

(8)   Ventilating fans for battery compartments should be so constructed and be of material such as to minimise risk of sparking in the event of the impeller touching the casing. Impellers of non-metallic material should be such that sparking due to static discharge is minimised.

(9)   Ducts should be made of a corrosion-resisting material or their interior surfaces should be painted with electrolyte resistant paint.

(10)   Any fan motor associated with a duct used to exhaust air from a battery compartment should be placed external to the duct and the compartment.

(11)   All openings through battery compartment bulkheads or decks, other than ventilation openings, should be effectively sealed to reduce the possibility of escape of gas from the battery compartment.

14.13 Electrical installations in battery compartments

(1) Switches, fuses, and other electrical equipment likely to cause an arc, should not be placed within the battery compartment.

(2) Luminaires within the battery compartment are to be of a type certified for hydrogen atmospheres.

(3) Cables, with the exception of those apertaining to the battery or the local lighting, should not be installed in battery compartments except where installation in other locations is impracticable when they should be either:

  (i) in seamless steel conduits or equivalent without joints or junction boxes and arranged to maintain the gas-tight integrity of the battery compartment; or,
  (ii) in accordance with 23.5.3 with an electrolyte resisting impervious non-metallic sheath applied over the metallic covering.

Sealed Batteries

14.14 Location

Sealed lead acid batteries and sealed nickel-cadmium batteries may be placed in the same compartment.

14.15 Ventilation

Ventilation to avoid the accumulation of flammable gas should be provided where boost charging facilities are installed.

14.16 Electrical installations in battery compartments

Electrical equipment may be installed within a compartment containing sealed batteries; such electrical equipment need not be suitable for use in hazardous areas.

Charging Facilities

14.17 For floating service or any other condition where the load is connected to the battery whilst it is on charge, the maximum battery voltage should not exceed a safe value for any connected apparatus. The voltage characteristics of the generators or rectifiers which will operate in parallel with the batteries should be suitable for each application.

14.18 Where apparatus capable of operation at the maximum charging potential is not available, a voltage regulator or other means of voltage control should be provided.

14.19   Where sealed batteries are installed in accordance with 14.16 and 14.18, a device independent of the normal charging arrangements should be provided to prevent gas evolution in excess of the manufacturer's design quantity.

14.20   A suitable warning plate should be fitted to the charger stating:

"Switch off charger before working on battery connections".

14.21   Where a low voltage battery is floated on the line with a resistor in series, all connected apparatus should be capable of withstanding the line voltage to earth. A suitable warning plate should be fitted stating:

"Disconnect charging circuit before working on any circuit connected to the battery".

14.22   For an emergency supply battery, the arrangements for automatic transfer switching should be such that the emergency supply is available whether the battery is on charge or not.

14.23   Except as provided below, the charging facilities for any battery should be such that the completely discharged battery can be completely charged in a reasonable time having regard to the service requirements. Extra-low voltage batteries provided in duplicate for communication supply (one in service, the other on charge) should be charged at a rate commensurate with the average discharge rate.

14.24   For lead acid batteries which normally stand idle for long periods, trickle charging should be provided to prevent permanent damage due to sulphation on self discharge.

14.25   Suitable means, including an ammeter and a voltmeter, should be provided for controlling the re-charging of each battery and to protect against discharge of the battery into the charging circuit.

SECTION 15

LIGHTING

15.1　Lamps should conform, as regards the type of lamp-cap, mechanical qualities and insulation resistance, to the requirements of BS 161, BS 1853, BS 3677, BS 5971, or other appropriate British Standard, except that lamps of 150 watts and over should be fitted with Medium Edison Screw (E 27) or Goliath Edison Screw (E 40) caps as appropriate. Luminaires should comply with BS 4533. All luminaires and their accessories must be designed to withstand the vibration encountered under normal service conditions.

15.2　Lampholders for tungsten filament lamps

(1)　For tungsten filament lamps, lampholders should be of the standard types shown in Table 15.1, and should normally be used on low voltage and extra low voltage circuits only.

(2)　Tungsten filament lamps having a rating exceeding those shown in Table 15.1 should not be fitted in the type of lampholder indicated.

(3)　Miniature lampholders E 10 should not be used for circuit voltages in excess of 24 V and small lampholders B 15s, B 15d and E 14 should not be used for circuit voltages in excess of 130 V, unless they are of ceramic or are insulated from earth.

Table 15.1　IEC designation for lamp-caps and lampholders

Description 1	Designation 2	Max. Size of Lamps (watts) 3	Max. Voltage of Circuit 4
Bayonet:			
Normal (BC)	B22	100	250
Small (single contact) (SCC)	B15s	—	130
Small (double contact) (SBC)	B15d	—	130
Screw:			
Goliath (GES)	E40	1500	—
Medium (ES)	E27	200	—
Small (SES)	E14	—	130
Miniature (MES)	E10	—	24

(4)   In bathrooms, washplaces, laundries, galleys and similar places, those parts of a lampholder likely to be touched by a person replacing a lamp should be constructed of or shrouded in insulating material, and fitted with a protective shield.

NOTE: The use of totally-enclosed luminaires is desirable.

(5)   Moulded insulated bayonet-type (B 22) lampholders should be of T2 temperature rating, see BS 5042.

(6)   Where centre-contact bayonet or Edison screw lampholders are used on single pole and earthed neutral systems, the outer or screwed contact should be connected to the neutral conductor.

(7)   Lampholders should not be connected to circuits having excess-current protection of rating exceeding the appropriate value stated in Table 15.2. This recommendation does not apply where lampholders and their wiring are enclosed in earthed metal or incombustible insulating material, or where separate fuse protection is provided.

Table 15.2   Excess-current protection of lampholders

Type of Lampholder	Maximum rating of fuse or miniature circuit-breaker protecting the circuit (amperes)
Small bayonet (B15)	6
Bayonet (B22)	16
Miniature Edison	
Screw (E10)	2
Small Edison Screw (E14)	6
Edison Screw (E27)	16
Giant Edison Screw (E40)	16

15.3   Lampholders for tubular fluorescent lamps (except for Ex 'e' type luminaires) should be bi-pin and comply with BS 6702. Lampholders should either adequately support the tube to withstand normal service vibration or, alternatively, the tube must be separately supported.

15.4   Lampholders for high pressure mercury discharge and metal halide lamps should be as follows:

Lamp Type	Holder	IEC Lamp Cap Designation
High pressure mercury (MBF) and metal halide (MBI) up to 125W	ES	E27
High pressure mercury (MBF) and metal halide (MBI) 250W and above	GES	E40
Linear metal halide (MBIL)	R7s	R7s

15.5   Lampholders for sodium lamps should be as follows:

Lamp Type	Holder	IEC Lamp Cap Designation
Low pressure (SOX) (SOX-E)	BC	B22
High pressure (SON and SON-T):		
up to 70 W	ES	E27
100 W and above	GES	E40
High pressure linear (SON-L)	R7s	R7s

15.6   Lampholders for Tungsten Halogen lamps should be as follows:

Lamp Type	Holder	IEC Lamp Cap Designation
Tubular 100 W and 150 W	ES	E27
Linear 100 W to 1500 W	R7s	R7s
Linear 2000 W	Fa4	FA4

15.7   Thermal requirements of luminaires should be in accordance with BS 4533. The cable connected to a lampholder terminal of a tungsten lamp luminaire should be insulated or sleeved to withstand 150°C continuously, e.g. glass or silicone rubber insulated.

15.8   Lamps in positions involving more than ordinary risk of mechanical damage should be installed in luminares of substantial construction and should be protected against such damage.

15.9   Enclosures for lamps of all types, including shades or guards, should be of materials which do not support combustion in accordance with BS 4533.

All lamps should be so placed or so guarded as to prevent ignition of any flammable materials.

15.10   All luminaires should be appropriate for the service they are required to perform and the definitions used to describe them should be as defined in BS 4533.

15.11   Portable luminaires

(1)   Portable luminaires for the illumination of decks, holds, engine rooms and similar spaces should be provided with lampholders which are either completely shrouded in insulating material or so protected by metallic guards insulated from the holders that all live parts cannot be touched.

(2)   Open-type portable handlamps should comply with BS 4533, Part 102, Section 102.8.

15.12 Masthead, side and stern light lanterns and lamps should be of a type acceptable to the Department of Transport.

15.13 In order to ensure readiness of operation, luminaires intended to provide emergency lighting in compliance with the requirements of SOLAS should form a part of the normal lighting system. Such emergency luminaires should bear a distinguishing mark for identification. Switches for emergency lighting should be inaccessible to passengers.

15.14 Luminaires intended to provide supplementary emergency lighting on RoRo passenger ships should be of a type approved by the Department of Transport.

> NOTE 1 Fluorescent lighting may be used for emergency lighting provided it can be shown that it will operate satisfactorily (including re-striking) at such reduced voltage of supply and at such lower limits of temperature as may be expected to occur in an emergency.

> NOTE 2 For emergency lighting of radio rooms see Part 2, 1.3(2).

Low Voltage Discharge and Fluorescent Lighting

15.15 Every inductor, capacitor and starter should comply with the following British Standard, as appropriate: BS 2818, BS 3772, BS 4017, BS 4782.

Where control gear is mounted remotely from the lamp, i.e. not within a luminaire, any metal case, where used, of individual components should be earthed and the terminals shrouded or enclosed. This apparatus should be fixed as close to the lamp as practicable in an accessible and ventilated position.

15.16 Lamps and lamp auxiliaries intended to operate on frequencies other than 50 Hz or 60 Hz or from d.c. supplies should achieve similar safety and, where possible, performance requirements as specified in all the appropriate British Standards.

15.17 Circuits should be capable of carrying the total steady current, viz. that of the lamp(s) and any associated gear and also their harmonic currents. Where more exact information is not available, the demand in volt-amperes may be taken for the purpose of this clause as the rated lamp watts multiplied by not less than 1.8. The neutral conductor in every discharge lighting circuit should be of the same cross-sectional area as that of the phase conductor(s).

> NOTE: The multiplier referred to in 15.17 is based on the assumption that the power factor of the circuit is not less than 0.85 lagging and there are no significant harmonic currents due to the generator wave form and the ship's load. See also 1.4(1).

100

High Voltage Discharge Lighting and Signs

15.18   Discharge lighting installations using voltages exceeding 650 V r.m.s. measured on open circuit, should comply with BS 559.

NOTE: In all high voltage discharge lighting circuits, particular attention must be paid to all aspects of safety, especially accessibility by unauthorised persons, provision of danger notices and effective means of isolation.

SECTION 16

HEATING AND COOKING APPLIANCES

16.1 Electric heating and cooking appliances should comply with the relevant requirements of BS 3456 and BS 4167.

General Requirements

16.2 The heating elements should be of materials durable at the highest temperature which they attain in normal service and should be so arranged that they can readily be replaced.

16.3 Microwave ovens should be fitted with a thermal protection device to interrupt the supply to the oven in the event of overheating, for example, should a timer failure occur as required by BS 3456, Part 102, Section 102.25.

16.4 All combustible materials in the vicinity of heating and cooking appliances should be protected by suitable non-combustible and thermal-insulating materials.

16.5 Every heating and cooking appliance, whether portable or fixed, should be controlled locally by a fixed switch; where a socket-outlet is provided it should be connected between the switch and the appliance. Control switches when in the "off" position should isolate the heating elements in all non-earthed poles.

16.6 A means by which power to the galley can be cut off in the event of fire should be fitted outside the galley exits in positions not likely to be made inaccessible by such a fire.

16.7 The position of fuses, switches and other control elements fitted near the appliance should be such that they will not be subject to temperatures above that for which they are designed and they should be accessible for inspection.

16.8 Earthing terminals at appliances, whether portable or fixed, should be effectively connected to earth.

Special Requirements for Galley Equipment

16.9 Cooking and heating appliances and their control equipment fitted in galley spaces should have splashproof enclosures (IP X4 to BS 5490). Enclosures should be corrosion-resistant.

16.10 Combined heating and cooking appliances should be of such construction that the live parts of the different sections are mechanically separated and that, when replacing components on one section, no live parts of the other section can be touched.

16.11 Portable cooking appliances should be of such shape or so weighted that they cannot easily be overturned. Suitable stowage positions should be provided.

Special Requirements for Space Heating Appliances

16.12 Space heaters should be of the convector type, except that heaters of the visible element type may be used provided they are designed and installed in such a manner as to minimise the risk of fire.
   Portable space heating appliances should not be used. It is desirable that space heaters should be equipped with means to interrupt the current if the temperature exceeds the permissible limit.

16.13 Space heaters should be durable and all parts should be of strong construction. All screws and nuts should be effectively locked.

16.14 Space heating appliances should be so designed and installed that clothing, curtains or other materials cannot be so placed as to cause risk of fire.

16.15 Space heating appliances should be so mounted that there will be no risk of dangerous heating of the deck or bulkhead or other surroundings.

Special Requirements for Trace and Electric Surface Heating Systems

16.16 Trace heating systems should comply with the relevant clauses of BS 6351, Parts 1, 2 and 3.

16.17 Systems should meet the requirements of service Category 22 in Table 1 of BS 6351, Part 2 and be provided with over-current protection, residual current protection with trip indication, adequate means of isolating the system from the supply and over-temperature limitation as required by that Standard and be to the satisfaction of the Appropriate Authority.

16.18 Cable or tape units should be provided with either metallic sheath, braid or wire armour.

16.19 The cable or tape units should be supplied from an isolating transformer or transformers with secondary circuit earthed and having a secondary voltage not exceeding 254 volts.

16.20 The residual current operated circuit breaker should comply with BS 4293 and should have a trip current no greater than 30 mA.

103

16.21 In situations where the cable or tape units are liable to mechanical damage they should be provided with suitable protection.

16.22 Notices are to be provided indicating the location of cables or tapes and warning personnel not to stand on traced pipes, etc.

16.23 Trace heating systems which are installed in hazardous areas should additionally be certified to BS 5501, Part 6 (Increased Safety Ex 'e').

SECTION 17

SEMICONDUCTOR CONVERTORS FOR POWER PURPOSES

17.1   For monocrystalline convertors, such as germanium and silicon, precautions should be taken to guard against the effects of transient over-voltages, see BS 44l7.

17.2   Semiconductor convertors should be rated for their operational duty having due regard to the system transient or peak loading requirements and the thermal capacity of the semiconductor devices.

17.3   For convertors operating in parallel with other convertor equipment, d.c. generators or batteries, precautions should be taken to ensure that, within the specified loading conditions, load sharing is such that overloading of any unit does not occur and that the combination of the paralleled equipment is stable.

17.4   When necessary, convertors should be capable of feeding regenerative power into the supply system. When this is not possible alternative means should be provided to absorb the regenerative power.

17.5   Where convertors which are force ventilated supply essential services, it should be possible to operate at reduced power on failure of a fan.

17.6   Where convertors are pipe ventilated or closed air-circuit ventilated, means should be provided for measuring the temperature of the cooling air after it has circulated through the equipment and to operate an alarm if this exceeds a pre-determined safe value or in the event of an air flow failure.

17.7   Where cooling water is used, consideration should be given to detection of leakage in an equipment enclosure and provision of an alarm indication. In addition the flow of coolant should be monitored to operate an alarm in the event of loss of flow.

17.8   Anti-condensation heating should be provided.

17.9   Where there are several convertors on the same supply system, means should be provided to decouple the device firing circuits in order to minimise mutual interference.

17.10   Sufficient line reactance should be provided to prevent the voltage dips during commutation having an unacceptable influence on other consumers. In addition the subtransient reactance of the supply system and the convertors should be such that the harmonics produced by the convertor on the system wave form comply with the system specification under all operating conditions.

17.11 When filters or capacitors are used to compensate reactive currents, changes of supply system frequency should not cause unacceptable increases of the r.m.s. and peak values of the system voltage.
Fuses used in filter circuits should be monitored.

17.12 Interference should remain within the limits specified in BS 1597 and special measures may have to be taken to prevent unacceptable conductor borne interference levels being transmitted to other parts of the ship, particularly by control cables, see 1.4(1).

NOTE: Attention is drawn to EMC problems which can arise with rectified supplies. Advice should be sought from the rectifier manufacturer regarding the output characteristics; reference should also be made to Appendix D and BS 5260.

17.13 For the purposes of inspection, cleaning and repair, provision should be made for access to and replacement of the semiconductor devices and fuses.

SECTION 18

TRANSFORMERS FOR POWER AND LIGHTING

18.1   This Section applies to all transformers for power and lighting and, where appropriate, to reactors.

NOTE 1   Transformers for high voltage discharge lighting should comply with BS 559. See also Section 15.

NOTE 2   Safety isolating transformers should comply with BS 3535. See also Appendix B.

18.2   Transformers for power and lighting, other than those in Notes 1 and 2 of 18.1, should comply with BS 171, excepting that Table III and Table IV of Part 2 of that Standard should be replaced respectively by Table 18.1 and Table 18.2 of this Section.

Table 18.1   Temperature rise for dry type air cooled transformers

Part	Insulation class & max. operating temperature °C	Maximum temperature rise °C measured by resistance method	
		Ocean going ships, see 1.10(1)	Outside tropical belt, see 1.10(2)
Windings	A (105°C)	50	55
	E (120°C)	60	65
	B (130°C)	70	75
	F (155°C)	90	95
	H (180°C)	110	115
	C (220°C)	140	145
Cores, metallic parts and adjacent materials		The temperature should in no case reach a value that will damage the core itself, other parts or adjacent matrerials	

NOTE: Where the specified cooling air temperature exceeds the value given in 1.10(1) or 1.10(2) as appropriate, the permitted temperature rise should be reduced by the amount of the excess temperature. No correction shall be made if the cooling air temperature is lower than that specified.

Table 18.2 Temperature rise for liquid-immersed type transformers

Part	Maximum temperature rise °C				
	Cooling class as defined in BS 171	Ocean going ships, see 1.10(1)		Outside tropical belt, see 1.10(2)	
		Measured by resistance	Measured by thermometer	Measured by resistance	Measured by thermometer
Windings, irrespective of insulation class	LNAN ⎫ LNAF ⎭	55	—	60	—
	LNWN ⎫ LNWF ⎭	65	—	70	—
Top liquid					
When the transformer is equipped with a conservator or sealed.	All	—	50	—	55
When the transformer is neither equipped with a conservator nor sealed.	All	—	45	—	50
Cores, metallic parts and adjacent materials	The temperature should in no case reach a value that will damage the core itself, other parts or adjacent materials.				

NOTE: Where the specified cooling medium temperature exceeds the value given in 1.10(1) or 1.10(2) as appropriate, the permitted temperature rise should be reduced by the amount of the excess temperature. No correction should be made if the cooling medium temperature is lower than that specified.

18.3 Reactors should comply with BS 4944 except that where reference is made to BS 171 the amendments in 18.2 should apply.

18.4 The regulation of transformers should take into account the maximum voltage drop allowed by 11.4(4).

18.5 Transformers, except those for motor starting, should be double-wound, i.e. separate windings.

18.6 Preference should be given to the use of dry type transformers.

18.7 Liquid cooled transformers should utilise a non-toxic coolant which does not readily support combustion. Where the coolant system is in a closed circuit, means of relieving excess pressure should be provided. An alarm should be provided to give indication that the pressure-relief device has operated. Where provision is made for breathing, a suitable desiccator should be provided. Suitable means should be provided for cooling and for containing all the liquid which might escape from a damaged tank or operation of the pressure-relief vent. For transformers located in machinery spaces, the containment may be reduced to a dimension which is considered adequate by the Appropriate Authority.

18.8 Isolation

(1)   Means should be provided for isolation of secondary windings which can be connected to a source of voltage.

(2)   When transformers are arranged to operate in parallel, means should be provided for isolation of the primary and secondary windings.

(3)   A suitable warning label indicating the points of isolation should be provided near the point of access.

18.9 Where forced cooling is used, it should be possible to operate at reduced power on failure of a pump or fan. Consideration should be given to the provision of suitable temperature indicating and alarm facilities.

18.10 Where liquid cooling is used, consideration should be given to the detection of leakage into the enclosure and provision of an alarm indication. In addition, flow of coolant should be monitored to operate an alarm in the event of loss of flow.

SECTION 19

ACCESSORIES

19.1 General requirements

(1) Accessories should be so designed and constructed that the passages for insulated conductors are of ample size and are free from rough projections, sharp angles and abrupt bends. All outlets for cables should have well-rounded edges or be suitably bushed.

(2) Accessories should be so designed and the insulated conductors should be so installed, that stress cannot be applied by the conductors to any terminal to which the conductors may be connected.

(3) Accessories should be so designed and fixed that dust and moisture cannot readily accumulate on live parts and their insulation.

(4) Cable entries should conform to the class of enclosure of the accessory.

19.2 Enclosures should be of metal which is, or has been rendered, corrosion resistant or of flame-retardant insulating material. Where electrolytic corrosion may occur between a metal enclosure and the surface upon which it is mounted suitable insulating material should be inserted and separate means should be provided to bond the case to earth.

19.3 Switches should comply with the relevant requirements of BS 3676.

(1) In galleys, laundries, bathrooms, machinery and other spaces where moisture may be present, switches should be in accordance with the relevant degree of protection given in Table 1.1 or of all-insulated construction.

(2) On weather decks, switches and their cable entries should be in accordance with the relevant degree of protection given in Table 1.1.

(3) Every switch or other means of control or adjustment should be so situated as to be normally inaccessible to a person using a fixed bath or shower. This requirement does not apply to electric shaver supply units complying with BS 3052 or to insulating cords of cord operated switches.

(4) Every switch not specially designed to break an inductive load of its full rated capacity should, if used to control a discharge lighting circuit, have a current rating of not less than twice the total steady current which it is required to carry or, if used to control filament lighting and discharge lighting, have a current rating of not less than the sum of the current flowing

110

in the filament lamps and twice the total steady current flowing in the electric discharge lamps.

19.4 Socket-outlets and plugs should comply with the relevant requirements of BS 196, or BS 1363 or BS 4343, as appropriate, see 7.3(3).

(1)   The live parts of socket-outlets should be so proportioned that their average temperature does not exceed that of the surrounding air by more than 30°C when the normal working current is flowing through them continuously.

(2)   Socket-outlets should be so constructed that they cannot readily be short-circuited. It should not be possible for any pin of the plug to be engaged with any live contact of its associated socket-outlet while any other pin of the plug is completely exposed.

(3)   Where differing distribution systems supplying socket-outlets are in use, the socket-outlets and plugs should be of such design that an incorrect connection cannot be made.

(4)   All 3-phase socket outlets should be of the same phase rotation.

(5)   The electrical clearances of the socket-outlets and plugs not interlocked with switches should be such that a short-circuit cannot be initiated if the plug be normally withdrawn from the socket while a current 50% greater than that for which it is rated is flowing at rated voltage.

(6)   Socket-outlets for a rated current in excess of 16 A should be interlocked with a switch such that the plug cannot be inserted or withdrawn when the switch is in the "on" position.

(7)   Where socket-outlets with earthing are required, the earthing contacts should make contact in advance of the live contact pins when inserting a plug.

(8)   "Watertight" plug and socket-outlet combinations should be of robust construction and be in accordance with the relevant degree of protection given in Table 1.1, and should retain that degree of protection when the plug is removed.
    Where a loose cover is used for this purpose, it should be anchored to its socket-outlet, e.g. by means of a chain. When the plug is inserted into its socket-outlet, the combined fitting and the interlocking switch, if any, should also be "watertight".

(9)   Socket-outlets should not be installed below the floor of machinery spaces and in closed fuel and lubricating oil separator rooms.

(10)   In a space containing a fixed bath or shower, there should be no socket-outlets and there should be no provision for connecting a portable appliance except where it is a shaver supply unit complying with BS 3052.

(11)   Socket-outlets for use with electric shavers should be incorporated in a shaver supply unit complying with BS 3052 when installed in bathrooms or wash places. When installed in other locations, they should be of a type specified in BS 3052, and be clearly marked with the words:

"For shavers only"

and be provided with a suitable current-limiting device.

(12)   Plugs should have provision for connections to be so made that no strain is transmitted to the terminals and contacts. The plugs or socket-outlets should be so designed that when in place they will be held in positive contact.

(13)   Every plug containing a fuse should be non-reversible and so designed and arranged that no fuse can be connected in an earthed conductor.

(14)   Where the supply is direct current, each socket-outlet should be controlled by a switch immediately adjacent thereto or combined therewith. Where the supply is alternating current and the plug is readily withdrawable such a switch need not be provided, except as required in 19.4(6).

SECTION 20

COMMUNICATIONS AND NAVIGATIONAL AIDS

20.1 General

The requirements of this Section relate to the following:

(i) Equipment for radio communication and navigation either by atmospheric path or via satellite
(ii) Automatic pilots, helm indicators, telegraphs, clocks, etc.
(iii) Manual and automatic alarms for crew or passengers and bell and / or call systems.
(iv) Telephone and teleprinter circuits, closed circuit television and television and loudspeaker systems

20.2 The radio and navigational equipment should be so installed and such precautions taken in the installation of equipment in the ship, as to ensure the proper operation of these services and to the requirements of all the relevant Statutory Instruments listed in Part 2.

20.3 Equipment should comply with the performance standards required by Department of Transport Type Approval specifications where they are applicable and comply with the requirements of BS 1597 with regard to levels of conducted and radiated interference.

20.4 The electrical installation of all equipment should be carried out in accordance with the recommendations in Appendix D and BS 7027 in order to achieve and maintain electromagnetic compatibility between systems.

20.5 Where the equipment of several systems is grouped in close proximity it should be installed so as to be protected from physical damage and contamination from adjacent systems during normal and / or fault conditions.

20.6 Safety and maintenance

(1) All items of equipment, accessories and cables should be of robust design and so installed as to ensure an ample margin of safety and reliability in operation under both normal and fault conditions.

(2) Equipment which must operate under automatic or remote control should do so without danger to personnel who may be in close proximity.

(3) As a minimum, warning notices should be provided in equipment areas where there is danger from shock, radio frequency burns and other injuries from radiation including X-rays.

113

Adequate means of isolation should be provided, preferably interlocked, to prevent accidental shock or exposure to radiation during maintenance.

(4)   Antennae and open wire feeders should be so placed and guarded as to be inaccessible to unauthorised personnel.

(5)   Communal antennae for broadcast reception should have facilities for isolation, muting and / or protection.

SECTION 21

CONTROL AND INSTRUMENTATION

21.1   General

This Section deals with electrical, electronic and programmable equipment and systems intended for control, monitoring, alarm and protection.

> NOTE: Control and instrumentation details are also included in Section 25.

21.2   General requirements

(1)   Operation

Operation of the control equipment should be simple to perform.

(2)   Reliability

Each apparatus should possess a degree of reliability in accordance with the importance of the control system of which it forms part.

(3)   Safeguarding

The design of the control equipment should be such that a failure in the control equipment will lead to the least dangerous condition of the controlled process and, furthermore, such failure should not render any reserve automatic or manual control inoperative. See also 1.5.

> NOTE: The least dangerous condition should be predetermined in terms of priority for the safety of the ship and may generally be taken as the least critical one for the main components and auxiliaries of the propulsion / manoeuvring plant.

(4)   Supply arrangement

As far as practicable, control and instrumentation circuits and their supply arrangements should be so designed that a failure of any of the associated power supplies does not damage the installation nor endanger the ship.

(5)   Stability

Each automatic control system, together with its controlled process, should be stable throughout its range of operation.

(6)   Repeatability and accuracy

The repeatability and accuracy of instruments and control equipment should be adequate for their proposed use and should be maintained at their specified value during their normal operative use and for the duration of their expected lifetime.

(7)   Segregation

Protection (safety) systems should be continuously available and, as far as possible, fully independent and separate from other control and alarm systems.

21.3   Environmental and supply conditions

(1)   General

In addition to the general requirements of Section 1 of these Recommendations, control and instrumentation equipment should be suitable for the conditions given in IEC 92-504, Clauses 22 to 30.

(2)   Power supplies

    (i)   All circuits providing emergency services should receive supplies from sources which are available under normal and emergency conditions.
    (ii)   In the event of failure of supply to the engine-room telegraph, indication should be given on the bridge.
    (iii)   Supplies to programmable electronic systems should be in accordance with 21.8(6).

(3)   Electromagnetic compatibility

    (i)   Each system should incorporate, as necessary, suitably screened equipment, earthing and arrangement of cabling to ensure that any induced interference between systems in no way impairs the proper effective operation of these systems at all times.

    NOTE: Precautions may have to be taken against multiple earthing.

    (ii)   Where systems are connected to a common source of supply they should be so arranged that no detrimental effects are induced on to the supply which could impair the operation of other apparatus connected on the supply.
    (iii)   Equipment should meet the requirements of BS 1597 and BS 7027. Further guidance on electromagnetic compatibility is given in Appendix D and in IEC Publication 533.

21.4   Design, construction and installation

Control and instrumentation components and systems and their installations should meet the requirements of IEC 92-504, Clauses 31 to 74.

21.5 Specific installations

(1) Fire detection, protection and extinguishing

(i) Fire detection, protection and extinguishing systems should meet the applicable requirements of SOLAS, see Part 2, 1.2.

(ii) Fire protection control installations, when fitted, should meet the requirements of IEC 92-504A, Clauses A1 to A4.

(2) Gas detection

Gas detection equipment should meet the applicable requirements of the IBC Code or IGC Code, see Part 2, 1.1 NOTE 3.

(3) Machinery alarms

Machinery alarm systems, when fitted, should meet the requirements of IEC 92-504A, Clauses B1 to B8.

(4) Machinery controls

(i) Machinery controls should meet the requirements of SOLAS, see Part 2, 1.1.

(ii) Where automatic controls for power supply generation are fitted they should comply with IEC 92-504A, Clauses C1 to C7.

(iii) Where automatic starting controls for electrically driven auxiliaries are fitted they should comply with IEC 92-504A, Clauses D1 to D6.

(5) Machinery protection

Machinery protection (safety) systems should meet the requirements of SOLAS, see Part 2, 1.1.

(6) Valve controls

Where valves for systems such as bilge or ballast are operated by remote or automatic control the following requirements should be met:

(i) Remote indication should be provided to show actual valve position or whether the valve is fully open or closed.

(ii) Actuator power failure should not permit a valve to move to an unsafe position.

(iii) Standby means, e.g. local manual, should be provided for operating the valves.

(iv) Valves and associated equipments located in positions liable to flooding should be capable of submerged operation, the enclosure 'degree of protection' being suitable for the anticipated submersion head.

(v) Valves for bilge systems should be capable of operation via controls outside the flooded area to meet the requirements of SOLAS, see also Part 2, 1.1.

117

21.6   Periodically unattended machinery

Additional requirements for periodically unattended machinery spaces are given in SOLAS, see Part 2, 1.1.

> NOTE: For reduced attendance the applicability of the above Regulations is determined by the Appropriate Authority.

21.7   Documentation, commissioning and testing

Control and instrumentation equipment and systems should meet the requirements of IEC 92-504, Clauses 75 and 76. See also Section 27.

21.8   Computer based systems

(1)   General

These clauses give specific recommendations for computer based systems, see Section 28, which are additional to those contained in other parts of this Section.
Documentation for computer based systems used for essential functions should be provided in accordance with BS 5515.

(2)   Safety applications

Computer systems which also provide safety functions (or in the event of their failure would have safety implications affecting the ship, its personnel or the environment) and which are not backed-up by non-computer based devices should be subjected to a comprehensive "failure mode and effects analysis". The results of this analysis are to be to the satisfaction of the Appropriate Authority.

> NOTE: To meet the desired availability the design configuration may require features such as redundancy and separation or diversity. Further guidance is available in Health & Safety Executive publication, see Part 2, 5.6.

(3)   Hardware modularity

The equipment should be so designed that the modules can be replaced readily, see also 21.8(8). Calibration and adjustment carried out using the instrumentation and documentation on board are considered acceptable.

> NOTE: Bench repair down to component level which requires specialist skills and test equipment is not normally expected to be possible on board.

(4)   Memories

Application program and data held in the system(s) should be protected from corruption due to loss of power, i.e. stored in non-volatile memory (ROM) or a volatile memory with a secure no-break supply.

(5)   Ancillary devices

Devices such as floppy discs, magnetic tape and cartridge discs should be suitably protected for use in the marine environment.

NOTE: These devices are particularly vulnerable to dirt, dust, heat, vibration, magnetic fields, mechanical impact, etc.

(6)   Power supplies

(i)   Means should be incorporated, as far as practicable, to protect the system against:

— accidental reversal of power supply polarity;
— voltage spikes;
— harmonic interference.

NOTE: The total harmonic distortion of the power supply should be no more than 5%. Where the generated power source exceeds this value the necessary filtering should be provided at the utilisation equipment.

(ii)   Where redundancy is required the following paragraphs should apply:

(a) Power supplies to processors should be arranged to provide automatic transfer facilities from the normal to an alternative supply of suitable quality, e.g. smoothed and stabilised when necessary.
(b) Operation of transfer arrangements should not interrupt or interfere with the safe operation of the ship.
(c) Attention should be given to:

— battery capacities;
— battery charging arrangements;
— inverter arrangements;
— system loading;
— system protection;
— earthing arrangements;
— output busbar arrangements of power distribution;
— synchronising arrangements to permit transfer of redundant or bypass systems.

(7)   Computer communications

(i)   Network topology

System architecture should be so arranged that any essential functions will continue to operate satisfactorily in the event of a

119

communication failure between any work station or computer and other parts of the network. If data links are redundant they should be as far apart as geographically practicable.

Computers situated in other geographical locations may act as back-up for a failed computer providing the main data link is not overloaded.

(ii)   Communication protocols

The communication protocol should be suitable for the intended application with respect to traffic rate and priority. See also 21.8(9)(iii) and (iv).

NOTE: Further guidance can be found in IEC Publications 954 and 955.

(iii)   Function priorities

When computer based systems are interconnected in data networks and include functions such as condition monitoring, stock inventory, planned maintenance and administrative routines, etc., special precautions should be taken to ensure the normal operation of essential functions.

(8)   Monitoring and fault diagnosis

(i)   Computer based systems should be self monitoring as far as practicable. Faults causing loss of an essential function should be detected, as far as practicable, and an alarm given. See also 21.2(3).

NOTE: This should include cyclic redundancy checks and watchdog routines. Spare digital and analogue inputs can be used for checking system operation and power supplies.

(ii)   The location of a fault should be indicated to a level compatible with the systems' designed replacement / repair policy.

NOTE: The optimum level of modular design, spares holding and fault diagnosis facilities will depend on the particular application and should be agreed between supplier and purchaser.

(iii)   Interconnected systems should be capable of testing the communication links and the data exchange management.

(9)   Man machine interface

(i)   General

At least two means of information presentation and command should be provided for all essential functions. One of these may be non-computer based.

(ii)   Command devices

Error in the normal operation of input devices, e.g. keyboards, should not cause computer failure, loss of stored data or alteration of programs.
The switch-over function to a standby system, if provided, should be simple to execute.

(iii) Visual display units

The presentation of information, e.g. mimic diagrams, should be in accordance with ergonomic principles.

NOTE: Colour distortion may be experienced due to the ship's magnetic field.

The maximum time delay for the creation of new display pages should be agreed between supplier and purchaser taking into account the importance of the functions described thereon.

(iv) Alarms

When an alarm essential for the safety and propulsion of the ship is activated the alarm channel should be displayed within 2 seconds and clearly described.
In colour graphic systems the means of distinguishing between unacknowledged and acknowledged alarms should not be by colour only.
Where the only indication of alarm monitoring is via video display, a separate indication on the screen should be dedicated for that purpose which allows all current alarm conditions to be viewed at all times by the operator.

(10)   Software

(i) Development and verification

The user (specification) requirements, design, implementation, test and maintenance phases of applications software should be developed in a documented methodical fashion permitting independent audit (i.e. quality assurance) for verification purposes.

NOTE: Further guidance on the production of highly reliable software can be found in IEC Publication 880.

(ii) Expert systems

When intelligent knowledge based systems, (see Section 28) are provided they are not to be used for closed loop real time control of safety critical functions.

(iii)   Security

Access for alteration to program or data should have effective security arrangements.

Change of parameters which alter system performance (e.g. control parameters, time constants) should only be possible by personnel authorised for this type of operation for the systems in question by means such as key arrangements or the use of dedicated codes, etc. Consideration should be given to the automatic print-out of the changes on the data logger or alarm printer.

Access to computer applications software should be highly restricted and any alterations of programs after validation should be notified to the Appropriate Authority.

(11)   Infant mortality precautions

Electronic modules, assemblies and PC cards, including spares and repaired units, that serve essential functions should have sufficient "burn-in" time to prevent failures due to infant mortality.

Generally, the equipment should be subject to an equivalent of 72 hours at 70°C with power connected to the device. Alternatively, consideration may be given to the manufacturers' quality assurance system.

(12)   Testing

Factory tests should include functional and electrical tests on modules and sub-assemblies including spares.

Factory and / or on-board commissioning validation tests on complete systems (i.e. integrated hardware and software) should be carried out to a programme agreed between supplier and purchaser including, where applicable:

— transfer of monitoring or control responsibility between workstations;
— alarm blocking functions;
— alarm acknowledge procedures;
— activation of relevant data communication links;
— functional testing of workstations;
— simulation of internal and external faults, including power supply variations, failure and restoration.

(13)   Manuals

Manuals should include instructions for operator initiated test routines and the use of any special purpose test equipment necessary to enable a defective module to be located and identified, the procedures for replacement of faulty modules and the setting-to-work of replacements. Special attention should be drawn to the procedures necessary to avoid program corruption by:

— test probes causing short-circuits;

122

— temporary removal of electromagnetic screening;
— inadequate protection against electrostatic discharges.

(14)   Spares

An appropriate policy regarding the quantity and future availability (including software support) should be agreed between supplier and purchaser. See also 21.8(3).

At least one printed circuit board of each type included in the computer system(s) for essential functions should be provided on board.

SECTION 22

LIGHTNING PROTECTION

22.1 General

(1)   Primary structural damage can result from an attachment of lightning to ships which do not provide a path of low conductivity to earth for the passage of lightning currents, e.g. ships of non-metallic construction or those having substantial non-metallic members.

(2)   Secondary damage, to ships' structures or to electrical systems, can result as an indirect consequence of a lightning attachment to a ship or its immediate vicinity. A path to earth of low conductivity may not avoid consequence of secondary damage which may occur as a result of high values of induced or resistance drop voltages produced by the passage of lightning currents.

Primary Protection

22.2 Protective systems

(1)   A protective system should include air terminals, down conductors and earth terminations so installed as to minimise the possibility of voltages being induced into electric cables due to the passage of lightning currents. See also 22.6(6).

(2)   A protective system need not be fitted to ships of metallic construction where a low conducting path to earth will be inherently provided by masts, structural members and hull.

(3)   A protective system should be fitted to any ship of non-metallic construction or one having substantial non-metallic members.

(4)   Metallic masts and structural members may form part or all of any protective system.

(5)   Metal rigging shrouds may act as fortuitous down conductors and should be bonded to the protective system.

(6)   Joints should be accessible and be located or protected so as to minimise accidental damage. They should be made by means of copper rivets or clamps. Clamps may be of copper or copper alloy and should preferably be of serrated contact type.

124

(7)   The resistance measured between air terminals and earth terminals should not exceed 0.02 ohm.

(8)   Suitable means should be provided to enable ships when in dry dock, or on a slipway, to have their protective systems or metal hull connected to an efficient earth on shore.
Connecting cables to the shore earth should be external to the ship throughout their length.

22.3   Air terminals

(1)   An air terminal should be fitted to each non-metallic mast.

(2)   Air terminals should be made from copper or copper alloy conducting bar of not less than 12 mm diameter, and project at least 300 mm above the mast top.

22.4   Down conductors

(1)   Down conductors should be made of copper, copper alloy tape or cable. Cable is preferred since the insulation and circular shape both inhibit surface discharge.

(2)   Down conductors should have a minimum cross section of 70 mm², be solidly secured to the structure and be run as straight as possible between air terminal and earth plate. Bends, where necessary, should have a minimum radius of ten times the equivalent diameter of conductor.

22.5   Earth terminals — See also 2.6

(1)   An unpainted lightning earth plate not less than 0.25 m² in area should be installed below the light-load water line so as to remain immersed under all conditions of heel. It should be provided with pillars to facilitate cable connections.

(2)   Earth plates should be of copper or other conducting material compatible with sea water. The establishment of electrochemical corrosion cells with other immersed metallic fittings should be avoided.

Secondary Protection

22.6   General

On all ships, whether metallic or non-metallic, equipment should be installed so as to limit the effects of secondary damage to the electrical system.

(1)   Metallic enclosures should be earthed to the metal hull or to the protective system. Particular attention should be paid to navigation lights and other equipment at the top of masts or elevated structures.

(2)   Cable screens or armour, though normally earthed for signal interference suppression, should not provide the sole lightning earth for equipment.

(3)   Lightning earth connections to the protective system should follow the most direct route.

(4)   The formation of cable loops, or metallic loops such as pipework, in proximity to down conductors should be avoided. Cables in close proximity to down conductors should be installed in substantial metal pipes.

(5)   On metal ships, cables along decks should be installed close to the decks to minimise the cross-sectional area of loop described between cable and deck. When choosing cable routes along decks advantage should be taken of the screening effect of earthed metallic structures near or above the cable runs, e.g. handrails, pipes, etc.

(6)   Means should be provided for the discharging to earth of any lightning energy that may induced in radio and navigational equipment antennae. Consideration should be given to the installation of transient protective devices such as spark gaps or surge divertors.

SECTION 23

TANKERS FOR OIL
AND OTHER SHIPS
WITH SIMILAR HAZARD

23.1 General

(1)   This Section details the additional precautions to be taken in the design of electrical installations onboard tankers intended for the carriage in bulk of oil cargoes (oil tankers) and provides guidance for other types of ships where oil or liquids of similar hazards are processed, handled or stored (other ships), e.g:

— oil recovery ships;
— offshore support ships;
— naval replenishment ships;
— ships built or converted for production, processing or storage purposes, where the recommendations for oil tankers are not appropriate.

(2)   They do not apply to those types of ships for which the hazardous areas and the electrical equipment permitted in such areas are defined in Statutory requirements, see Part 2, 1.1 and 1.7.

23.2 Safety concepts

(1)   The safety concepts of this Section presupposes that:

   (i) Electrical equipment is installed and maintained in accordance with BS 5345 except as amended by this Section.
  (ii) Electrical equipment and cables are provided with suitable overload and short-circuit protection.
 (iii) Electrical equipment and its component parts are constructed so as to guard against electrical and mechanical failure in the intended condition of use, particular attention being given to the need for protection against weather, the ingress of liquids and particulate matter, corrosion, condensation, the effects of solvents and the effects of heat from adjacent plant.
  (iv) Storage tanks, process plant, pipelines, flanges, valves, etc., are designed and installed to the satisfaction of the Appropriate Authority.
   (v) The ship as a whole is adequately maintained to sustain the integrity of the original design.

(2)   They do not cover for fire and explosion risks emanating from:

   (i) Catastrophic failures such as the rupture of a bulk storage tank, process vessel or a pipeline.
  (ii) Ignition sources other than those associated with electrical equipment.
 (iii) Applications where flammable material is burned, e.g. in a boiler, gas turbine or diesel engine.
  (iv) Ignition of explosive materials.
   (v) Ignition of combustible dust or fibres.

128

(3)   The degree of hazard and the extent of the hazardous areas are based on established marine practice. The aft machinery spaces, the accommodation and the enclosed bridge are normally considered to be non-hazardous, provided that the Statutory requirements for the location and separation of such spaces have been met, see Part 2, 1.1. Nevertheless, it is possible for these spaces to become contaminated by gas or vapour. Additional precautions, which are outside the scope of these Recommendations, should be incorporated in formal operating instructions.

23.3   Hazardous areas

(1)   Liquids having a flash point temperature not exceeding 60°C (closed cup test).

The hazardous areas / spaces related to oil or other liquids of similar hazard having a flash point temperature not exceeding 60°C are defined in Tables 23.1 (oil tankers) and 23.2 (other ships), but the following general principles should be applied:

Hazard Category A —   Areas / spaces in which flammable gas / air mixture is continuously present or present for long periods.

Hazard Category B —   Cofferdams adjoining oil cargo tanks. Spaces which are separated by a single bulkhead from storage tanks and which have no mechanical ventilation system.

Hazard Category C —   Cargo pump rooms of oil tankers. Spaces having mechanical ventilation which are separated by a single bulkhead from storage tanks but where the mechanical ventilation may not be in continuous operation whilst the ship is in a non-gas free condition.

Hazard Category D —   Areas / spaces in which flammable gas / air mixture is likely to occur in normal operation.

Hazard Category E —   Areas / spaces in which flammable gas / air mixture is not likely to occur in normal operation, and if it occurs it will exist only for a short time.

129

NOTE 1   The definitions of Hazard Categories A, D and E are synonymous with Zones 0, 1 and 2 respectively, as defined in BS 5345. However, the permitted electrical equipment is limited to that defined in Tables 23.1 and 23.2.

NOTE 2   Hazard Categories B and C are based on established marine practice and are not covered by the zonal concepts defined in BS 5345.

(2)   Liquids having a flash point temperature exceeding 60°C (closed cup test).

It is considered that oil or liquids of similar hazards having a flash point temperature exceeding 60°C do not present any particular hazard from flammable or explosive gases / vapours insofar as electrical equipment is concerned, therefore, no hazardous zones are nominated. It is, however, deemed advisable to minimise potential sources of ignition by the adoption of the following:

(i)   Control and / or monitoring circuits which are in direct contact with cargo products in the tanks and / or pipelines should be intrinsically safe — Ex 'ia'.
(ii)   Luminaires and electric motors driving pumps, and which are located in a cargo pump room, should be of a certified safe type.
(iii)   Any portable electrical equipment to be used in cargo tanks should be of a certified safe type.

Ships intended and built for the sole carriage in bulk of oil or liquids of similar hazards having a flash point temperature exceeding 60°C should under no circumstances be used for the carriage of other types of flammable cargo nor should they be used for the carriage of cargoes which are heated to within 15°C of their flash point temperature.

(3)   Enclosed and semi-enclosed spaces with direct access into a hazardous area.

An enclosed or semi-enclosed space with direct access into a hazardous area which is of a greater hazard than the considered space should be regarded the same hazard category as the space or area into which the opening leads. An enclosed space in the interior of which there is no internal release of flammable gases or vapours, but which has access to a Hazard Category D or E area may be considered non-hazardous in the case of 'other ships' (see Table 23.2) if the relevant requirements of Table 23.3 are complied with.

(4)   Extension of hazardous areas

During loading, discharging and ballasting operations and during gas freeing by mechanical means, gases / vapours may be present on the open deck outside the hazardous areas defined in Tables 23.1 and 23.2. To cater for this condition, exposed electrical equipment located on open deck and on

130

superstructures which could be in use during such operations, e.g. luminaires, winches, bridge wing apparatus, etc., should be of a type which ensures the absence of sparks or arcs and of hot spots during its normal operation or be of a certified safe type.

Equipment of other types should be provided with means of isolation, all of which should be grouped together and located in a non-hazardous space so that such equipment can be isolated during cargo handling, ballasting and gas freeing operations.

Consideration should also be given to the equipment located in spaces forward of the cargo or storage tanks which are below the level of the main deck and have a direct opening onto the main deck. Such equipment should be similar to the types as described above for open deck unless the following arrangements are provided:

(i)   self-closing air-lock doors are provided for the entrance(s) onto the main deck and that these entrance(s), together with all other openings to the space(s), including ventilating inlets and exhausts, are sited at least 5 m from the foremost cargo tank or 10 m measured horizontally from any cargo tank ventilation outlet, whichever is the greater;

(ii) the spaces are mechanically ventilated and failure of the ventilating system is indicated by an audible alarm at a normally manned station.

23.4   Ventilation

(1)   Ventilation of hazardous spaces

Where the selection of electrical equipment in hazardous spaces is conditional on the space being ventilated, the ventilation systems should comply with the following requirements:

(i)   they should be such as to minimise the possibility of air stratification ventilate non-hazardous spaces;

(ii) they should be such as to minimise the possibility of air stratification and the formation of air pockets;

(iii) attention should be given to the ventilation inlet and outlet locations and air flow in order to minimise the possibility of cross contamination;

(iv) outlet ducts should not be routed through non-hazardous areas: where this is not practicable, the ducting should be of a robust design;

(v) the system should be sufficient to give at least 12 air changes per hour. It should be noted that for reasons other than the selection of electrical equipment, higher rates of air changes per hour may be required, e.g. SOLAS Chapter II-2 Regulation 59.3 specifies a minimum of 20 air changes per hour for the cargo pump rooms of oil tankers.

(2)   Pressurising of spaces

The ventilation systems of spaces maintained at an overpressure to prevent the ingress of gases / vapours should comply with the requirements detailed in

Table 23.3. In addition, the following requirements should be complied with:

(i) they should be completely separate from those systems used to ventilate hazardous spaces;

(ii) they should be such as to minimise the possibility of air stratification and the formation of air pockets;

(iii) inlets and outlets should be located in non-hazardous areas and as far away from sources of hazard as is reasonably practical;

(iv) inlet ducts should not be routed through hazardous areas: where this is not practicable, the ducts should have an overpressure in relation to the hazardous area or, alternatively, the ducting should be of a robust design and gas tight with respect to the hazardous area.

23.5 Electrical installations

(1) Selection of equipment

Protection against electrical ignition is best achieved by installing electrical equipment outside hazardous areas. Where this is not practical for operational reasons, the electrical equipment should only be of a type permitted by Tables 23.1 and 23.2 for that location and should be suitable for the gas grouping and temperature class of the atmospheres involved. The construction and type testing should be in accordance with the relevant National or International Standard.

NOTE 1   Electrical equipment for use in Hazard Categories A-D inclusive should be constructed and type tested in accordance with BS 229, BS 4683, BS 5501, or with an equivalent National or International Standard.

NOTE 2   Electrical equipment for use in Hazard Category E should, as a minimum, be constructed and type tested in accordance with BS 4683, Part 3, or with an equivalent National or International Standard.

Within the air locks as permitted in Table 23.3, luminaires and the prescribed monitoring and alarm equipment should be of a type as permitted for Hazard Category D.

Within the spaces protected by overpressure ventilation as described in Table 23.3, emergency luminaires and the prescribed monitoring and alarm equipment should be of a certified safe type. Other electrical equipment located within the space and which is required to operate on loss of pressure should be of a type permitted in the hazardous area into which the opening leads, see Table 23.2.

Within the ventilation ducting for hazardous spaces, electrical equipment should be of a type permitted in the space being ventilated.

Electric motors driving equipment located in Hazard Category C spaces should be installed in normally safe spaces, separated from the space by a gas-tight steel bulkhead or deck. Flexible couplings or other means of maintaining alignment should be fitted to the shafts between the driven equipment and

132

their motors and, in addition, suitable stuffing boxes should be provided where the shafts pass through the gas-tight bulkhead or deck.

(2)   Systems of supply

Earthed distribution systems should not be used, except that on systems designed to operate at over 3 kV, earthed systems may be acceptable where the value of neutral impedance is chosen to give an earth fault current $>3I_c$ where I_c is the per phase capacitive charging current for the system.
Hull currents which arise from those systems described in 4.4 and 5.3 are not considered to contravene the previous paragraph.

(3)   Electric cable installations

Cables passing through hazardous areas other than Hazard Category E, see Table 23.2, or serving electrical equipment in such areas, unless they form part of intrinsically safe circuits, are to include a metallic sheath or braid or wire armour for earth leakage detection, unless they are enclosed in a gas-tight steel conduit.
Cables associated with intrinsically safe circuits should only be used for such circuits and should be separated from other electric cables containing non-intrinsically safe circuits, e.g. not carried in the same casing or pipe nor secured by the same cable fixing clips. A minimum separation of 50 mm should be obtained wherever practicable. The provision of an individual cable for each intrinsically safe system is preferred. Where multicore cables are used, the cores of each intrinsically safe circuit should be enclosed in an individual conducting screen.
Cables, cable ducts and pipes should be suitably sealed where necessary to prevent any additional hazard arising due to liquids, gases or vapours which might otherwise pass along them.

(4)   Isolation of equipment

Equipment of a certified safe type requiring an electrical supply should be provided with effective means of isolation located in a non-hazardous space, clearly labelled to identify it with the equipment controlled. Effective means to prevent unauthorised operation of the isolating device resulting in restoration of the supply while any hazard exists should also be provided, except for intrinsically safe circuits.

(5)   Transmitting aerials

Transmitting aerials and any associated rigging should be installed in accordance with BS 6656.

(6)   Portable equipment

No facilities for connecting portable electrical equipment should be provided in hazardous areas and no trailing cables should be permitted except when the ship is gas free. Only self-contained battery operated equipment or turbo driven lamps, all of which should be of a certified safe type approved by an Appropriate Authority, should be provided for use in hazardous areas.

133

Table 23.1 Oil tankers intended for the carriage in bulk of oil cargoes having a flash point not exceeding 60°C (closed cup test).

Hazard Category	Description of Location	Typical Example	Permitted Certified Safe type Equipment / Cables
A	Cargo tanks and cargo piping.		(i) Intrinsically safe – Ex 'ia'. (ii) Other electrical equipment specifically approved for use in Zone 0 and acceptable to the Appropriate Authority. (iii) Only cables associated with the intrinsically safe apparatus referred to in (i) and the electrical equipment referred to in (ii).
B	Cofferdams (including permanent, i.e. segregated, ballast tanks adjacent to cargo tanks).		(i) Equipment / cables as permitted in Hazard Category A. (ii) Electrical depth sounding devices or log devices and impressed current cathodic protection system anodes or electrodes for external hull protection. These are to be housed in gas-tight enclosures sited clear of any cargo tank bulkhead. The associated cables are to be installed in steel pipes with gas-tight joints. NOTE 1 Gas-tight enclosures and gas-tight joints are to be to the satisfaction of the Appropriate Authority. NOTE 2 Where cofferdams can contain sea water, corrosion resistant metal pipes giving adequate mechanical protection should be used.
C	(i) Cargo pump rooms. Hold spaces with independant tanks. Enclosed or semi-enclosed spaces immediately above cargo tanks or having bulkheads above and in line with cargo tank bulkheads. Spaces other than cofferdams adjacent to and below the top of a cargo tank such as trunks, passage-ways and holds.		(i) Equipment / cables as permitted in Hazard Category B. (ii) Intrinsically safe – Ex 'ib'. (iii) Flameproof luminaires – Ex 'd'. (iv) Pressurised luminaires – Ex 'p'. (v) Flameproof alarm – Ex 'd'

Table 23.1 cont.

Hazard Category	Description of Location	Typical Example	Permitted Certified Safe type Equipment / Cables
C cont.	(ii) Enclosed and semi-enclosed spaces in which cargo hoses which have not been made safe are stored.		(vi) Cables associated with the permitted equipment. (vii) Through-runs of cable provided such cables are run in channels of steel section plate or in corrosion resistant metal pipes giving adequate mechanical protection.
D	(i) Areas on open deck within 3 m of cargo tank ventilation outlets which permit the flow of small volumes of vapour caused by thermal variation.		(i) Equipment / cables as permitted in Hazard Category C. (ii) Flameproof – Ex 'd'. (iii) Increased safety – Ex 'e' except motors. (iv) Pressurised – Ex 'p'. (v) Other electrical equipment specifically approved for use in Zone 1 and acceptable to the Appropriate Authority. (vi) Through runs of cable provided such cables are run in channels of steel section or in corrosion resistant metal pipes giving adequate mechanical protection and supported clear of the deck. Where cable expansions are to be located in these areas they should not be sited within 3 m of any gas or vapour outlet.
	(ii) Areas on open deck within 10 m of cargo tank ventilation outlets which permit the flow of large volumes of vapour during loading or discharging or ballasting.		
D continued on page 136	(iii) Areas on open deck within 3 m of openings to cargo or storage tanks.		

135

Table 23.1 cont.

Hazard Category	Description of Location	Typical Example	Permitted Certified Safe type Equipment / Cables
D cont.	(iv) Areas on open deck over all cargo tanks (including ballast tanks within the cargo tank block) to the full width of the ship, plus 3 m fore and aft of the cargo tanks on open deck, up to a height of 2.4 m above the deck.		
	(v) Areas on open deck within spillage coamings surrounding cargo manifold valves and 3 m beyond these and other coamings intended to keep spillages clear of accommodation and services spaces, up to a height of 2.4 m above the deck.	area of possible spillage / coaming	
	(vi) Areas within 2.4 m of the outer surface of a cargo tank where such a surface is exposed to the weather.		
	(vii) Areas on open deck within 3 m of openings to spaces of Hazard Categories B, C or D.	storage tank	

136

Table 23.2 Other ships where oil or other liquids having a flashpoint not exceeding 60°C (closed cup test) are handled, processed or stored.

Hazard Category	Description of Location	Typical Example	Permitted Certified Safe type Equipment / Cables
A	Inner spaces of containment systems and associated pipework, e.g.: Cargo / storage tanks. Process plant.		(i) Intrinsically safe – Ex 'ia'. (ii) Other electrical equipment specifically approved for use in Zone 0 and acceptable to the Appropriate Authority. (iii) Only cables associated with intrinsically safe apparatus referred to in (i) and with the electrical equipment referred to in (ii).
B	(i) Enclosed and semi-enclosed spaces which are separated by a single bulkhead from cargo / storage tanks and which have no mechanical ventilation system, e.g.: Cofferdams. (ii) Enclosed and semi-enclosed spaces in which pipes containing cargo are located and which have no mechanical ventilation system.		(i) Equipment / cables as permitted in Hazard Category A. (ii) Electrical depth sounding devices and log devices and impressed current cathodic protection system anodes and electrodes for external hull protection. These devices are to be housed in gas-tight enclosures sited clear of any cargo / storage tank bulkhead. The associated cables are to be installed in steel pipes with gas-tight joints. NOTE 1 Gas-tight enclosures and gas-tight joints are to be to the satisfaction of the Appropriate Authority. NOTE 2 Where cofferdams can contain sea water, corrosion resistant metal pipes giving adequate mechanical protection should be used.

137

Table 23.2 cont.

Hazard Category	Description of Location	Typical Example	Permitted Certified Safe type Equipment / Cables
C	(i) Enclosed and semi-enclosed spaces having mechanical ventilation and which are separated by a single bulkhead from cargo / storage tanks but where the mechanical ventilation may not be in continuous operation whilst the ship is in a non-gas free condition, e.g.: Cargo pump rooms. Hold spaces with independant tanks. Enclosed and semi-enclosed spaces immediately above cargo tanks or having bulkheads above and in line with cargo tank bulkheads. Spaces other than cofferdams adjacent to and below the top of a cargo tank such as trunks, passage-ways and holds. (ii) Enclosed and semi-enclosed spaces in which cargo hoses which have not been made safe are stored. (iii) Enclosed and semi-enclosed spaces in which pipes containing cargo are located and which are mechanically ventilated but where the ventilation may not be in continuous operation, whilst the ship is in a non-gas free condition.		(i) Equipment / cables as permitted in Hazard Category B. (ii) Intrinsically safe – Ex 'ib'. (iii) Flameproof luminaires – Ex 'd'. (iv) Pressurised luminaires – Ex 'p'. (v) Flameproof alarm – Ex 'd'. (vi) Cables associated with the permitted equipment. (vii) Through runs of cable provided that such cables are carried in channels of steel section plate or in corrosion resistant metal pipes giving adequate mechanical protection.

138

Table 23.2 cont.

Hazard Category	Description of Location	Typical Example	Permitted Certified Safe type Equipment / Cables
D	(i) Enclosed and semi-enclosed spaces separated by a single bulkhead from cargo / storage tanks and which have continuous mechanical ventilation, except when the ship is in a gas free condition, and loss of ventilation is alarmed at a manned station, e.g.: Pump rooms of storage barges. Pump rooms of oil recovery ships. Spaces separated by a single bulkhead from tanks of recovered oil on oil recovery ships. (ii) Enclosed and semi-enclosed spaces with closed process plant and associated valves and pipe flanges where: – valves are in frequent use and / or are of the packed gland type; – flange joints may be broken whilst the plant is not in a gas free condition; – the space is continuously ventilated except when the plant is in a gas free condition; – loss of ventilation is alarmed at a manned station. (iii) Enclosed and semi-enclosed spaces in which pipes containing cargo are located and which have continuous mechanical ventilation except when the pipes are in a gas free condition and loss of ventilation is alarmed at a manned station. (iv) Areas on open deck within 3 m of cargo / storage tank ventilation outlets which permit the flow of small volumes of vapour caused by thermal variation.		(i) Equipment / cables as permitted in Hazard Category C. (ii) Flameproof – Ex 'd'. (iii) Increased safety – Ex 'e' except motors. (iv) Pressurised – Ex 'p'. (v) Other electrical equipment specially approved for use in Zone 1 and acceptable to the Appropriate Authority. (vi) Through runs of cable.

D continued on page 140

139

Table 23.2 cont.

Hazard Category	Description of Location	Typical Example	Permitted Certified Safe type Equipment / Cables
D cont.	(v) Areas on open deck within 10 m of cargo / storage tank ventilation outlets which permit the flow of large volumes of vapour during loading or discharging or ballasting.		
	(vi) Areas on open deck within 3 m of openings in cargo / storage tanks.		
	(vii) Areas on open deck over all cargo / storage tanks (including all ballast tanks within the cargo tank block) to the full width of the ship, plus 3 m fore and aft of the cargo tanks on open deck, up to a height of 2.4 m above the deck.		
	NOTE: This area classiciation may be subject to special consideration when the total tank capacity is 3000 m^3 or less.		
	(viii) Areas on open deck within spillage coamings surrounding manifold valves and 3 m beyond these and other coamings intended to keep spillages clear of accommodation and services spaces, up to a height of 2.4 m above the deck.	area of possible spillage coaming	
	(ix) Areas within 2.4 m of the outer surface of a cargo / storage tank where such a surface is exposed to the weather.		
	(x) Areas on open deck within 3 m of: – valves in frequent use and / or valves are of the packed gland type; – flange joints which may be broken when the plant is not in a gas free condition.		
	(xi) Areas on open deck within 3 m of an opening to spaces of Hazard Categories B, C and D.		

Table 23.2 cont.

Hazard Category	Description of Location	Typical Example	Permitted Certified Safe type Equipment / Cables
E	(i) Areas on open deck within 3 m of process plant.		(i) Equipment / cables permitted in Hazard Category D.
	(ii) Areas on open deck within 3 m of: – valves which are infrequently used; – flange joints which are broken only when the ship is in a gas free condition.		(ii) Equipment of a type which ensures the absence of sparks or arcs and absence of ignition capable surfaces during its normal operation and acceptable to the Appropriate Authority.
	(iii) Enclosed and semi-enclosed spaces with closed process plant and associated valves and pipe flanges where: – valves are infrequently used; – flange joints are only broken when the plant is in a gas free condition; – the space is continuously ventilated except when the plant is in a gas free condition and loss of ventilation is alarmed at a normally manned station. NOTE: Open sample points should be subject to special consideration. (iv) Areas on open deck within 3 m of openings in spaces of Hazard Category E.	process/plant	(iii) Equipment specifically designed for use in Zone 2 and acceptable to the Appropriate Authority.

NOTE: The action to be taken on loss of ventilation should be incorporated in formal operating instructions. Such instructions are outside the scope of these Recommendations.

Table 23.3 Other ships – enclosed spaces with access to hazardous areas.

Access to and from Hazard Category	Typical Example	Requirements
A B C	NOT APPLICABLE	
D		(i) Access via air-lock consisting of two doors spaced at least 1.5 m but not more than 2.5 m apart. (ii) The space to have overpressure ventilation of approximately 5 mm wG in relation to the hazardous area. (iii) A pressure monitoring device to be fitted and arranged to initiate an audible alarm at a normally manned station and disconnection of non- certified safe type electrical equipment on loss of overpressure. (iv) An audible and visual alarm system to give warning on both sides of the air-lock doors to be provided to indicate if both doors are simultaneously in the non-closed position.
		(i) Access via a mechanically ventilated air-lock consisting of two doors spaced at least 1.5 m but not more than 2.5 m apart. (ii) The air-lock and the space to have overpressure ventilation of approximately 5 mm wG in relation to the hazardous areas, the ventilation systems being such that one fault will not result in the simultaneous loss of overpressure in the air-lock and space. (iii) Pressure monitoring devices to be fitted and arranged to initiate an audible and visual alarm at a normally manned station on loss of overpressure in the air-lock and the space. (iv) An audible and visual alarm system to give warning on both sides of the air-lock to be provided to indicate if one of the air-lock doors remains in a non-closed position after entry or exit of personnel.
E		(i) The space to have ventilation overpressure of approximately 5 mm wG in relation to the hazardous areas. (ii) A pressure monitoring device to be fitted and arranged to initiate an audible alarm at a normally manned station.

NOTE: The action to be taken in the event of loss of overpressure should be incorporated in formal operating instructions. Such instructions are outside the scope of these Recommendations.

SECTION 24

SYSTEMS OPERATING AT ABOVE 1 kV AC

24.1 General

(1)   This Section deals with the additional requirements for systems operating at voltages above 1 kV but not exceeding 15 kV.

(2)   The main switchboard should be in at least two independent sections, so arranged that duplicated services may be operated even in case of fault in one section of the switchboard.

(3)   Lower voltage systems supplied from the high voltage system should have adequate precautions taken to prevent the lower voltage system being charged by leakage from the high voltage system. Such precautions could, for example, be an earthed screen between the HV and LV windings on transformers or the LV system having its neutral earthed at the transformer.

(4)   Access to high voltage equipment by unauthorised personnel is to be prevented, e.g. by the provision of locks and keys, warning notices, etc.

NOTE 1   All keys provided for access should be available only to authorised personnel.

NOTE 2   Only authorised personnel should carry out maintenance, repair and calibration of high voltage equipment and the "permit to work" system is recommended, see BS 6626.

(5)   Suitable anti-condensation heaters should be considered for all equipment.

24.2   System earthing

(1)   Earthed neutral or insulated systems are acceptable but attention is drawn to the possibility of transient overvoltage to earth being higher on a high impedance earth system and on an insulated neutral system. See NOTE to C.3.2(3).

(2)   Earthing should be carried out through a resistor / impedance to limit the fault current to earth. Earthing resistors / impedances should be of such a value that the earth fault current is limited to a value not exceeding the full load current of the largest generator. The prospective earth fault current should be at least three times the value of current required to operate any earth fault protection devices.

143

(3)   Where an earthed system is divided into two or more sections, means for neutral earthing should be provided for each section.

(4)   All earthing resistors / impedances should be connected to the ship's hull. In addition earthing resistors / impedances should be bonded together on the hull side of the resistance / impedance.
    In order to eliminate possible interference with radio, radar and communication circuits, the means of bonding should be separate from that provided by the ship's hull.

(5)   Efficient means should be provided for indicating defects in the insulation of the system. An indicator should be provided unless earth leakage protection, or its equivalent, to provide automatic isolation, is used. In earthed systems, the indicator may be in the form of a low reading ammeter operated from a current trasnsformer in the neutral.

(6)   In high impedance earthed systems, where the total leakage current on an earth fault would exceed 5 A, earth leakage tripping should be arranged for the automatic isolation of defective circuits.

24.3   High voltage tests

(1)   All equipment should be subjected to appropriate high voltage tests. The test levels recommended apply equally to equipment intended to operate with either earthed neutral or insulated systems.

(2)   Machines*

(i)   Type tests

Random sample tests should be carried out to evaluate the basic design, type of material, manufacturing procedures and processes incorporated into an insulation system. Sample coils should adequately represent the configuration of the finished coil to be used in the winding, except that for convenience, the size of coil and number of turns may differ from a particular production batch.
    For this purpose the requirements of the random test specified in BS 4999, Part 144 should apply, except that the inter-turn insulation should be tested at U_n / 3 + 1000 volts a.c. r.m.s., where U_n is the rated line-to-line voltage.

(ii)   Routine tests

(a)   Inter-turn — A high frequency high voltage test should be carried out on the individual coils in order to demonstrate a satisfactory withstand level of the inter-turn insulation to steep fronted switching surges. This test should be carried out preferably after inserting the coils into the stator core and after bracing and wedging (if necessary with temporary wedges at the ends of the core).
    The test should be carried out by applying a sufficiently high

frequency to develop the required voltage across the coil, normally by discharging a capacitor acrosss the coil leads. The peak value of the test voltage is given by the formula:

$$U \text{ peak } = 3 \ U_n \sqrt{\frac{2}{3}}$$

Each coil should be subjected to at least five impulses of injected voltage. Should any coil fail during testing, it should be replaced and the inter-turn test applied to the replacement coil and repeated on those coils disturbed during the replacement.

(b)   Power frequency — A power frequency high voltage test should be carried out on the completed winding in accordance with BS 4999, Part 143, in order to demonstrate a satisfactory withstand level to earth.

* Tests for machines with vacuum impregnated windings are under consideration. In the meantime, tests should be agreed between the manufacturer and the purchaser.

(3)   Other   equipment

Other equipment should be tested in accordance with the British Standard listed in the appropriate section of these Recommendations for the apparatus concerned.

In cases where the rated voltage is outside that given in the British Standard or where no British Standard is quoted, a power frequency high voltage test should be carried out at the value given in Table 1 of BS 5622, Part 1.

24.4   Creepage   and   clearance   distances

The minimum creepage and clearance distances provided for all connections, terminals and similar bare "live" parts should be in accordance with the British Standard listed in the appropriate Section of these Recommendations for the apparatus concerned. In cases where the rated voltage is outside that given in the British Standard or where no British Standard is quoted, the following minimum creepage and clearance distances should be provided:

Nominal System Voltage	Minimum Clearance Between phases and to earth	Minimum Creepage Between phases and to earth
1 100	25 mm	25 mm
2 400	40 mm	40 mm
3 300	50 mm	50 mm
4 160	60 mm	70 mm
6 600	65 mm	90 mm
11 000	80 mm	125 mm
13 800	85 mm	140 mm
15 000	95 mm	150 mm

24.5   Cables and conductors

(1)   For cables for operation above 1 kV, see 10.3.

(2)   High voltage cables should be segregated, as far as practicable, from cables operating at lower voltages and all high voltage cables should be readily identifiable.

(3)   High voltage cables should not be run in the open through accommodation spaces. Elsewhere, they should be installed in accordance with (i) or (ii) below:

    (i)   In the open, e.g. on carrier plating or other approved cable support system, when they should be provided with a continuous metallic screen, or sheath, or armour which should be effectively bonded to earth to reduce danger to personnel. For systems up to and including 3.3 kV, the metallic screen or sheath may be omitted provided the cable is armoured.

    (ii)   Contained in earthed metallic ducting or pipe when the cables should be as in (i) above. Other cables should not be run in the same ducts or pipes as high voltage cables.

24.6   Switchgear, control gear, fuse gear

(1)   General

    (i)   Switchboards should comply with the requirements of BS 5227.
    (ii)   Low voltage and extra low voltage control circuits, junction boxes and fuses required for the operation of high voltage equipment should be segregated from the high voltage components.
    (iii)   Facilities should be provided to enable safe maintenance to be carried out in accordance with BS 6626, e.g. safety locks.

(2)   Switchgear

    (i)   Circuit breakers should be of the withdrawable type or with equivalent means or arrangements permitting safe maintenance whilst the busbars are live.
    (ii)   Integral means should be provided to earth isolated circuits so that cables, etc., are discharged.
    (iii)   Circuit breakers should comply generally with BS 5311.

(3)   Control Gear

Motor starters and controllers should comply generally with BS 587.

(4)   Fuse gear

Reference should be made to BS 2692 and BS 5907.

146

SECTION 25

ELECTRIC PROPULSION PLANT

25.1   General

(1)   The requirements contained in other Sections of these Recommendations apply, as appropriate, to electric propulsion plant except as qualified by the requirements of this Section.

(2)   The requirements of this Section relate to the electric propulsion equipment, including thrusters, and deal with the propulsion motors and thrusters, generators, their prime movers, electrical couplings, excitation circuits, semiconductor convertors and their cables and wiring, instrumentation, protection and control equipment.
  Any electrical equipment which may affect the propulsion or manoeuvrability of the ship and which is directly associated with the propulsion system should comply with the requirements of this Section.

25.2   Propulsion system performance

(1)   The torque available from the propulsion motors for manoeuvring should be such as to enable the ship to be stopped or reversed when the ship is travelling at its maximum service speed in a time to be agreed between the builder of the ship and the manufacturer(s) of the electrical propulsion equipment. This should be based on the estimated torque / speed characteristics of the propeller during manoeuvring and other necessary ship characteristics.

(2)   An adequate torque margin should be provided in propulsion systems for all operating conditions including rough weather, ice breaking, turning, etc., based upon the information provided regarding propeller and ship characteristics. Particular attention is drawn to motor pull-out.

(3)   In order to minimise excessive torsional stresses and / or torsional vibrations of excessive magnitude, careful consideration should be given to the co-ordination of the mechanical constants of the entire system including all prime movers, generators, convertors, motors, electrical couplings, gearing, shafting and propellers, together with the electrical characteristics of the system.

(4)   The electrical system should be stable under all operating conditions, due regard being paid to switching transients, system recovery after fault and / or maloperation. Operation of the protection equipment should also be reviewed under these conditions.

147

NOTE: Where generating sets also supply power to services other than propulsion, consideration should be given to the starting requirements of a.c. propulsion machines, such that this may be achieved within the limits of voltage and frequency transient values specified in Section 9, with an agreed minimum of plant available.

(5)   The capability of the prime mover and propeller shaft systems and seatings should be adequate to withstand the torques which would be developed under short-circuit conditions and those given in 25.2(4).

(6)   All necessary information regarding the equipment should be passed to the party responsible for the investigations specified in 25.2(1) to 25.2(5).

25.3   Prime movers

(1)   Where propulsion generators are required to operate in parallel the governing system should permit stable operation to be maintained over the entire operational load and speed ranges of the prime movers.

(2)   The rated power of the prime mover in conjunction with its load build up and overload capabilities should be adequate to supply the power required during both steady state and transient operating conditions of the electrical equipment. See also 25.2(1) and 25.2(2).

NOTE: Where exhaust gas driven turbine blowers are used to supercharge oil engines, special consideration may have to be given to the transient requirements.

(3)   The shaft system of the generator sets is to be capable of meeting the requirements given in 25.2(5) and 25.3(4) without damage.

(4)   The prime mover should be capable of absorbing regenerative power, for example, when the ship is manoeuvring from full ahead to full astern, without undue increase in speed. The amount of this increase should be agreed between the manufacturers of the prime mover and electrical machinery. Where the prime mover cannot absorb sufficient regenerative power to meet the performance requirements specified, means should be provided for limiting such power and / or absorbing the excess.

(5)   An emergency overspeed shutdown device should be provided. See also 25.9(1).

25.4   Electrical machines

(1)   Propulsion motors, generators, electrical couplings and their associated rotating exciters, if any, should comply with the requirements of BS 2949.

148

NOTE: Attention is drawn to variable speed machines where the temperature limits should not be exceeded under all agreed operating conditions, particularly at low speed, or high torque or any similar combinations.

(2)   Where machines are pipe ventilated or closed air-circuit ventilated, they should comply with 25.9(10).

(3)   Where cooling water is used, reference should be made to 1.14.

(4)   Anti-condensation heating should be provided. See also 25.9(11).

(5)   Propulsion machines should be capable of withstanding overspeeding up to the limit reached in accordance with the characteristics of the overspeed protection device at its normal operational setting. See also 25.3(5), 25.9(1) and (3).

(6)   Where forced lubrication (pressure or gravity fed) is used on propulsion machines, temperature and pressure or temperature and flow measuring devices should be fitted and arranged to operate an alarm if the temperature exceeds a predetermined safe value or in the event of oil flow failure. See also 25.9(12). An alternative means of lubrication such as oil rings or oil reservoir should be provided unless:

(i)   an automatically operated standby oil supply is provided or
(ii)   the period which elapses before the machine comes to rest after interruption of power does not exceed 30 seconds.

The lubrication of the bearings of propulsion motors, together with associated gearing and shafting, should be effective at all normal speeds from creep speeds upwards, both ahead and astern, having due regard to the ship's inclination and the angle of shaft rake. The shafts and bearings should not be damaged by slow rotation, whether or not electrical power is applied to the motor, or whether such rotation is induced by the propellers, and under all predictable oil temperature conditions. Separate means may be provided to prevent such damage due to slow rotation of the shaft, e.g. a shaft brake.

(7)   For instrumentation local to the machines see 25.7(4).

25.5   Excitation system

(1)   More than one means of excitation and associated control is to be provided for propulsion motors and generators. In systems with multiple motors and / or generators, the degree of excitation capacity and control provided is to be such that on the failure of any one component the plant may be operated at a reduced power level or at a level to be agreed by the purchaser.

(2)   The mechanical strength of shafts and couplings of exciters, and the power output of the driving machines should be suitable for the increased

149

output demanded during manoeuvring and short-circuit conditions in the main propulsion circuit.

(3)   The rating of static exciters and their supply should be suitable for the increased output demanded during manoeuvring or short-circuit conditions in the main propulsion circuit.

(4)   For protection requirements refer to 25.9(9).

(5)   Where loss of excitation occurs, for any reason, in a machine in a d.c. propulsion system, means should be provided to minimise damage to equipment and consideration should be given to means of restoring propulsion to the ship.

(6)   Excitation circuits whether supplied from auxiliary busbars or from rotating or static exciter sets should be provided with means for limiting the transient over voltages induced when the field circuits are opened.

(7)   Resistors which are connected across the excitation circuit of synchronous propulsion motors when they are operating asynchronously during starting and manoeuvring should be of such a value as to limit the voltage induced in the circuit, be insulated for this voltage and rated for the most onerous duty.

25.6   Cables and wiring

Conductors should consist of not less than 7 strands and the cross sectional area of any conductor should not be smaller than 1.5 mm². Interconnecting wiring of smaller cross section may be used for propulsion control systems with electronic equipment having very low short-circuit capacities such as computers. The mechanical properties of such cables, wiring and their terminating arrangements should not compromise the safety of the ship. Cables which are connected to the collector rings of synchronous motors should be adequately insulated for the voltage to which they would be subjected during manoeuvring, see 25.5(7).

25.7   Instrumentation

(1)   AC systems. The following instruments should be provided:

   (i)   An ammeter for each propulsion motor and generator.
  (ii)   A voltmeter, wattmeter and frequency meter (or tachometer) for each propulsion generator. Alternatively, in multigenerator systems, switched voltmeters and frequency meters may be used.
 (iii)   An ammeter for each exciter.
 (iv)   A speed indicator for each propeller shaft (for variable speed shafts) at each control station.
  (v)   A temperature indicator for reading directly the temperature of the stator windings of propulsion generators and motors. See also 25.7(3).

150

(2)   DC Systems. The following instruments should be provided:

(i)   An ammeter for each main circuit.
(ii)   A voltmeter for each propulsion generator, motor and exciter. Alternatively, voltmeters with selector switches may be used.
(iii) An ammeter for each exciter.
(iv)   A speed indicator for each propeller shaft at each control station. See also 25.7(3).

(3)   The instruments required by 25.7(1) and 25.7(2), as appropriate, should be mounted in the main control assembly or any other location if more convenient and should be clearly and indelibly labelled. See also 25.8.

(4)   Consideration should be given to providing local indication of cooling air or winding temperature and, where machines have oil lubrication, bearing temperature.

25.8   Control

(1)   A machinery control station should be provided at a location convenient for the operation of the propulsion plant. All controls, alarms and instrumentation necessary for operating the plant should be grouped together at this position.

NOTE: Control of direction by levers or hand wheels should be such that ship manoeuvre "Ahead" corresponds to pushing levers away from the operator or to the right or clockwise on rotation of hand wheels. For "Astern" the opposite should apply. In any case where the operator has a visual reference of the direction of motion, e.g. on the Bridge, then the direction of operation of levers and hand wheels should correspond directly to resulting motion of the ship.

(2)   The capability of delegating propulsion control to other stations may be provided when justified to ensure adequate viewing of the operation or activity of the ship.

(3)   The machinery controls at the delegated station should be simple and be capable of being exercised with the minimum of reference to instruments.

(4)   Where the propulsion equipment can be controlled from a number of control stations, a selector switch or similar, should be provided at the machinery control station to allow the manoeuvring control to be transferred to the delegated station. Simultaneous control of the propulsion equipment from two control positions should not be possible. Indication lights should be provided at each control station to indicate which station has control.

(5)   Transfer of machinery control to the delegated station should only be possible when its controller is either at "Stop" or co-incident with the controls at the machinery control station. Consideration should be given to an arrangement in which control must be accepted before transfer takes place.

(6)   The machinery control station should be able to resume control at all times. Transfer of control should be effected smoothly and without loss of time.

(7)   Where control of the propulsion machinery is from the navigating bridge, an emergency stopping device should be provided at that location to remove propulsion power from the ship.

(8)   In systems where remote control of the propeller is by control of prime mover speed or propeller pitch, control is also to be provided for use in emergencies.

(9)   Where the rotation of the propulsion motors or propeller shaft cannot be readily observed from the control station indicators should be provided.

(10)   The manoeuvring control equipment may be either manually operated or power assisted or a combination of both.
    In the case of manual operation, all manoeuvring switches, excitation regulators and controllers should be operable without undue effort.

(11)   If the power supply should fail in a power assisted control system, e.g. utilising electrical, pneumatic or hydraulic aid, it should be possible to restore control by other suitable means in a short time. Failure of the power supply to a control system should operate an audible and visible alarm.
    Failure of the power aid should operate an alarm indication and not result in the interruption of power to the propulsion system, or render the emergency "Stop" circuits ineffective.

NOTE: Where it is not possible to revert to full manual control in emergencies, consideration should be given to providing redundancy in equipment to enable a sufficient degree of control to be applied to ensure safety of the ship.

High integrity supplies should be provided for those systems that are essential to the safe operation of the ship.

(12)   In closed loop control systems special consideration should be given to ensure stability and reliability.
    The control system, should be fail-safe and designed to prevent the imposition of loads or speeds in excess of those for which the plant is designed.

(13)   All controls for operating prime movers, set up switches, contactors, excitation switches, etc., should be interlocked to prevent incorrect operation, e.g. opening of switches not intended to be operated while carrying current. Where static equipment is used for switching functions, similar interlocking features should be provided which should not be negated by loss of power supply. Interlocks should be provided to prevent the circuits for "Ahead" and "Astern" rotation being closed simultaneously.

(14)   Access doors for switchgear and control gear should be locked to prevent access while equipment is energised and provided with a key available only to authorised personnel.

(15)   All circuits, instruments and important apparatus should be clearly and indelibly labelled for rapid identification.

(16)   The coils of relays and contactors and resistors in series with them, if any, should be of substantial and reliable construction if their failure would result in interruption of the supply of power to the propeller shaft or initiate a condition likely to cause damage to the electrical plant. The number of such coils in a propulsion system and the number of auxiliary contacts in series with them should be kept to a minimum. Circuits supplying such coils should be separate and distinct from circuits supplying other apparatus.

25.9   Protection

(1)   The emergency overspeed shutdown device installed on the prime mover should be set to operate at a speed above the highest speed possible during periods of regeneration. The prime mover should be designed to withstand overspeeds up to the value imposed by this device. See also 25.3(4) and (5).

(2)   Where separately driven d.c. generators are connected electrically in series, means should be provided to prevent reversal of the rotation of a generator following failure of the driving power from its prime mover.

(3)   Where excessive overspeeding of the propulsion motors may occur, e.g. at light loads or on the loss of a propeller, suitable overspeed protection should be provided. See also 25.4(5).

(4)   Where there is a possibility of a propeller being blocked by ice or fouled by rope, etc., then consideration is to be given to the provision of stall protection to prevent damage to the driving motor.

(5)   Overcurrent protective devices, if any, in the main circuits should be set so that there is no possibility of their operating due to normal transient currents caused by manoeuvring or operation in heavy seas. See also 25.2(1) and (2).

(6)   Overcurrent protection should not be fitted in excitation circuits except as permitted by 25.9(9).

(7)   Short-circuit protection should provide rapid clearing of the circuit and / or suppression of system voltage (suppression of current in constant current systems).

(8)   Means for detecting earth current should be provided for the main propulsion circuit and this should be arranged to operate an alarm upon the occurrence of an earth fault. When the fault current flowing is liable to cause

serious damage to the electrical equipment, arrangements for tripping should also be provided or, in the case of an earthed d.c. system, the normal earth connection may be disconnected. Earth leakage devices should be arranged to function for specified earth fault currents.

(9)   Automatic circuit-opening devices should not be included in excitation circuits unless such devices form an essential part of the protection system for the main propulsion circuit. See also 25.9(6) and (7).

An overload alarm should be provided together with a time delay to prevent its operation during field forcing conditions. Excitation circuits should be provided with lamps, voltmeters, or other suitable means, to give a continuous indication of the state of the insulation of the excitation circuit under running conditions.

> NOTE: Where fuses are used for protection in the excitation system, they should not interrupt the field discharge circuit on rupturing.

(10)   Means should be provided for measuring the temperature of the cooling air after it has circulated through the equipment and to operate an alarm if this exceeds a pre-determined safe value or in the event of an air flow failure. See also 25.4(2) and 17.6.

(11)   Heaters should be provided in major items of propulsion equipment to prevent condensation when they are idle for appreciable periods.

(12)   A switch may, if desired, be provided for silencing the audible alarm(s) referred to in this Section to obviate the continuous sounding of the alarm; but in such a case a visual warning device should be automatically switched on to indicate acceptance of the alarm(s).

25.10   Testing

The following special tests should be carried out:

(i)   Work tests
As far as practicable, all normal acceptance tests of individual items of equipment should be carried out at the maker's works to show that they meet the requirements of these Recommendations. In addition to normal tests prescribed elsewhere in these Recommendations, all protective devices should be tested to show that they are electrically and mechanically satisfactory.

(ii)   Dock and sea trials
Complete tests should be carried out including duration runs and manoeuvring tests which should include reversing the ship from full speed ahead to full speed astern, tests for operation of all protective devices and stability tests for control. All tests necessary to demonstrate that each item of plant and the system as a whole are satisfactory for duty should be performed.

(iii) Insulation testing
Immediately prior to and after trials the insulation resistance and temperature of the propulsion machines should be measured and recorded.

SECTION 26

DYNAMIC POSITIONING

26.1 General

(1)   A dynamic positioning (DP) system is defined as all equipment necessary to provide means of controlling the position and heading of a ship within predefined limits by means of resultant vectored thrust.

(2)   The DP control system is defined as the control computer(s), the input sensors (including manual control of set points) and output actuators, together with associated cabling and power supplies.

(3)   Ships should have declared means of main propulsion and steering which may form part of the DP system and which, at least, comply with applicable regulations for the main propulsion and steering systems.

(4)   A single fault condition within the DP control system should not cause loss of propulsion or steering capability.

In addition, where redundancy is required (see Part 2, 5.7) a single fault condition within the DP system should not cause total loss of positioning or heading capability.

26.2   Thrust systems

(1)   Each thrust unit should be provided with independent means of stopping the motor from the control stations.

(2)   Electric power to each thrust unit should be supplied by individual circuits without the use of common feeders or common protective devices.

(3)   Each thrust unit should have an independent control system with power supplied by individual circuits without the use of common feeders or common protective devices.

(4)   Thrust units need not have the same failure mode of operation but for all potential failures, the failure mode of each thrust unit and the reaction of the ship under these conditions, should be clearly defined.

(5)   Propeller blade pitch angle and azimuth angle of steerable units, defined for the failure mode, are to remain static on failure without subsequent drift. Resetting of thruster operation is to require manned intervention.

(6)   Attention should be paid to limiting effects of interference on

156

command and feed-back signals between thrusters, their control systems and the DP system. See also Appendix D.

In addition, where redundancy is required 26.2(7) to 26.2(12) should apply.

(7)   Systems should be arranged to minimise common mode failure.

(8)   Each electric and hydraulic control system should be provided with duplicate power supplies arranged through individual circuits without the use of common feeders or common protective devices.

(9)   Circuits should be arranged for automatic transfer in the event of failure of the normal power supply but need not be exclusive to the supply of thrust control power.

(10)   Operation of transfer arrangements should not cause a power supply failure mode to be initiated.

(11)   More than one feed-back signal channel should be provided between thruster, thruster control system and the programmable electronic system. As far as practical, feed-back channels are to be independent of common mode failure, e.g. two position feed-back channels would require independent sensors, preferably not activated by the same actuator arm, and independent signal cables which should be segregated throughout their length.

(12)   Feed-back signals of differing parameters are preferred, e.g. position, power consumption, current consumption. The DP system should be capable of comparing these signals, initiating alarms on failure and be capable of continued operation on a different signal, see Table 26.1. Validation techniques should be used to identify malfunctions in signal channels.

26.3   Control system power supplies

Power supplies to the DP control system processors should be in accordance with 21.8(6).

26.4   Reference systems

(1)   The following systems should be provided, interfaced with the central or distributed processor units:

(i)   Position reference.
(ii)   Heading reference.
(iii)   Wind reference.
(iv)   Attitude reference (VRU), where attitude reference is required for automatic position keeping.

In addition, where redundancy is required, 26.4(2) to 26.4(5) should apply.

(2)   Systems for position, heading, wind and attitude reference should be

157

duplicated, attention being given to segregation and minimising common mode failure.

(3)   Each duplicated system should preferably be capable of simultaneous on-line operation.

(4)   Each duplicated system should be provided with alarms to indicate failure of that system and misalignment between systems, see Table 26.1.

(5)   Power supplies to each duplicated system should be arranged through separate circuits; each provided with short-circuit protection.

26.5   Computers

(1)   Computers should not be installed in any area where performance could be adversely affected by changes in environmental conditions.

(2)   Where it is necessary to provide an air conditioned environment for the computers, and where redundancy of system operation is required, temperature alarms should be fitted and provision made for an alternative source of air conditioning facilities.
In addition, where redundancy is required 26.5(3) and 26.5(4) should apply.

(3)   The computer and associated alarms, display units and programmable systems should be duplicated and segregated so as to minimise common mode hardware failure.

(4)   Transfer of operation to the duplicate computer should be automatically accomplished without disturbance to the controlled position and heading.

26.6   Cable installations

(1)   Particular attention should be paid to segregating signal, command and interface cables from all sources of interference. See also Appendix D.

(2)   Signal command and interface cables and their terminations should be positively identified throughout their length.

26.7   Communications

Means of direct communication should be provided between all positions from which any aspect of DP operation can be controlled.

26.8   Control stations

(1)   Indication of the following, where applicable, is to be provided at each station (other than portable joystick) from which automatic station keeping can be controlled:

158

(i) The heading and position of the vessel relative to the desired reference point.
(ii) Thrust output, individual and total.
(iii) Angular position of steerable thruster units.
(iv) Operational status of reference system sensors.
(v) Environmental conditions, e.g. wind speed and direction.

(2)   Provision should be made at main control stations and subsidiary control stations from which it is possible to control the dynamic positioning system to indicate which station is in control.

(3)   Control of the dynamic positioning system is to be possible from only one station at a time.

(4)   Changeover between control stations is to be arranged so that it may only be effected with the acceptance of the station taking control. The system is to be provided with interlocks or other suitable means to ensure effective transfer of control.

(5)   Means of communication are to be provided between main control stations, subsidiary control stations, the navigating bridge and machinery space control stations.

26.9   Control consoles

Attention should be given to ergonomic aspects and 26.9(1) to 26.9(9) should apply.

(1)   Buttons and controls for similar services and functions are to be grouped together in a clear and logical format.

(2)   For important control parameters, where operation of buttons or controls will result in a change of position or heading, a positive action is required, e.g. such control buttons should be fitted with covers or require to be pressed twice to initiate the action.

(3)   Joysticks should have a positive and easily found "off" position, i.e. detent, at the central position which requires a positive action to disengage.

(4)   All motion displays and, preferably, mimic diagrams should be aligned with the ship.

(5)   An alternative means of manual control of thrust units which does not depend on use of the automatic control systems should be provided, on or adjacent to the control console.

(6)   Changeover equipment and changeover procedures are to be incapable of maloperation and are to have a clearly defined failure mode.

(7)   Position and heading displays together with the alarms enumerated in Table 26.1 are to be incorporated.

In addition, where redundancy is required, 26.9(8) and 26.9(9) should apply.

(8)   Status of operation of major units within the DP system should be displayed and alarms provided to detect change of state of such units.

(9)   Failure of the changeover equipment required by 26.9(6) should not cause changeover to occur.

26.10   Alarms

(1)   Means should be provided to retain "first fault" indication.

(2)   Alarms should be structured to distinguish between statements that inform and conditions that require urgent action to be taken.

Table 26.1

Item	Alarm	Remarks
On-line Computer	Failure	Automatic changeover (if standby fitted)
Heading	Off limit	
Position	Off limit	
Power Supply	Fault	
Position Reference System	Failure, Fault, Misalignment	For each position reference system
Gyro Compass	Fault, Misalignment	Automatic changeover (if standby fitted)
Attitude Reference Unit (VRU)	Fault, Misalignment	Automatic changeover (if standby fitted)
Wind Sensor	Fault, Misalignment (if standby fitted)	
Taut Wire Hydraulic Oil Pressure	Low	See NOTE
Taut Wire Hydraulic Oil Temperature	High	See NOTE
Taut Wire Hydraulic Oil Tank Level	Low	See NOTE
Taut Wire Excursion	Excursion limit	
Total Electrical Power Consumption	Excessive	Adjustable between 50-100% full load capacity
Computer Environment Air Conditioning	Temperature	
Major Units		See 26.9(8).

NOTE: These alarms may be grouped.

SECTION 27

TESTS OF COMPLETED INSTALLATION

27.1   Before a new installation, or alterations of or additions to an existing installation, are put into service the appropriate tests specified in 27.2 to 27.5 inclusive should be made. Such tests should be in addition to, and not in substitution for, the acceptance tests of the individual items of plant at the manufacturer's works.

> NOTE: These tests are intended to indicate the general condition of the installation at the time of completion; satisfactory test results do not, however, in themselves necessarily ensure that the installation is satisfactory in all respects. The importance of systematically inspecting and testing apparatus and circuits cannot be too strongly urged, and periodic inspections and tests are essential if the installation is to be maintained in a sound condition and undue deterioration is to be detected. All defects thus discovered should be made good without loss of time.

27.2   Insulation resistance

(1)   The insulation resistance should be measured, preferably by self-contained instruments such as a direct-reading insulation resistance tester applying an appropriate voltage.
When an insulation test is made on a circuit incorporating capacitors of a total capacitance exceeding 2 microfarads, an insulation tester of the constant-voltage type should be used in order to ensure that accurate test readings are obtained.

(2)   A test for insulation resistance should be applied to all permanent wiring of communications, lighting and power circuits between all insulated poles and earth and, where practicable, between poles. The installation may be sub-divided to any desired extent and appliances may be disconnected if tests give results lower than those in Table 27.1.

> NOTE: Attention is drawn to the importance of recording the temperature of machine windings at the same time as the insulation resistance is measured. The insulation resistance of machine windings varies considerably with temperature. Typical values are shown in Figure 27.1

(3)   A 500-volt insulation tester, arranged to indicate resistance in ohms, should be provided to enable periodic testing of insulation resistance to be carried out, and by plotting results converted at 40°C as shown in Figure 27.1 to detect any serious deterioration.

162

Table 27.1

Voltage (Nominal) of Circuit	Minimum Insulation Resistance in Megohms
Below 50 V	0.3
50V to 440V	1.0
Greater than 440V	$\dfrac{\text{Nominal Voltage}}{1000} + 1.0$

27.3 Earth continuity

(1)   Tests should be made to verify that all earth continuity conductors and earthing leads are connected to the frame of apparatus and to the structure, hull or general mass of earth and that socket outlet earthing terminals are connected to earth.

(2)   Where metal-sheathed cables, whether armoured or not, are used tests should be made to verify that all metallic envelopes are electrically continuous throughout their length, and are earthed as required by Sections 2, 11 and 24.

(3)   Where earthed systems are used, it should be verified that:

(i) Single pole control devices and fuses are connected in the live conductor only.
(ii) Wiring has been connected correctly to plugs and sockets.
(iii) The outer contacts of Edison screw-type lampholders are connected to the earthed conductor.

27.4 Earth fault loop impedance

Where protective measures are used which require a knowledge of earth fault loop impedance, the relevant impedances should be measured, or determined by an equally effective method.

27.5 Performance tests

(1)   All switchgear should be loaded as nearly as practicable to its working load in order to ensure that no overheating takes place due to faulty connections or incorrect rating. Switches and circuit-breakers should be operated on load to test their suitability and to demonstrate that the operation of all protective devices are electrically and mechanically satisfactory. The satisfactory operation of all interlocks is to be demonstrated.

163

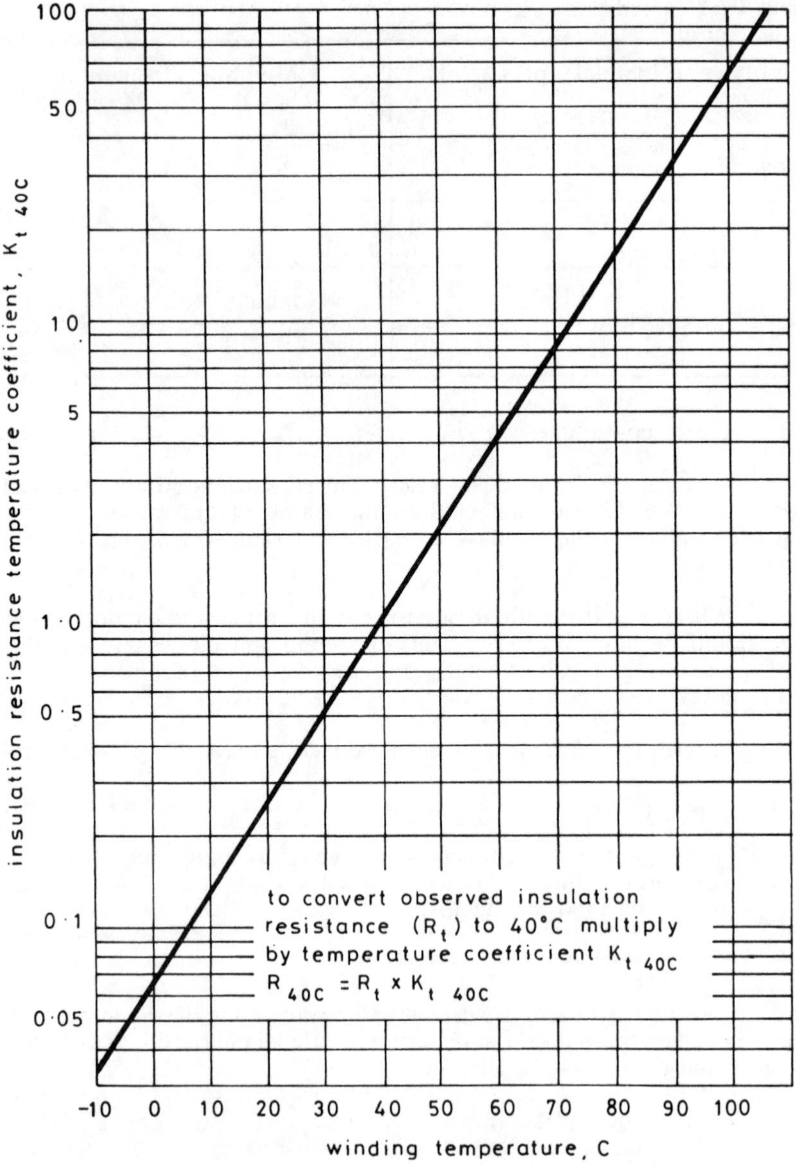
100
50
10
5
1·0
0·5
0·1
0·05
insulation resistance temperature coefficient, K t 40C
to convert observed insulation
resistance (R t) to 40°C multiply
by temperature coefficient K t 40C
R 40C = R t x K t 40C
-10
0
10
20
30
40
50
60
70
80
90
100
winding temperature, C

Reproduced by kind permission of the Institute of Electrical and Electronic Engineers Inc, U.S.A. from IEEE Standard 43-1974 Recommended Practice for Testing Insulation Resistance of Rotating Machines.

Figure 27.1 Recommended practice for testing insulation resistance of rotating machinery

(2)   All generator sets should be run over a sufficient range of load, including full rated load, or as nearly as practicable to full rated load, and for a duration sufficient to demonstrate that commutation, electrical characteristics, governing, range of excitation control, phase rotation, lubrication and absence of excessive vibration are satisfactory.

If sets are intended to operate in parallel they should be tested over a range of loads to demonstrate the following:

(i)   They are stable from 20% full load (kW) up to the total combined full load (kW), or as nearly as practical to the total combined full load of the group, and load sharing is satisfactory.
(ii) For a.c. generators — the kVA loads of the individual generating sets do not differ from their proportional share of the total kVA load by more than 5% of the rated kVA of the largest machine when operating at the nominal power factor of the system.

The voltage and speed regulation when the load is suddenly thrown on and off should be satisfactory.

Overspeed trips together with all other devices relative to the protection of the generator sets should be demonstrated to show that they are satisfactory.

Synchronising equipment and any associated protective devices should be demonstrated to verify correct functioning between each generating set and all other generating sets intended to operate in parallel. Reverse current, reverse power and overcurrent trips and any other safety devices should be satisfactorily demonstrated.

(3)   Each motor, together with its associated control gear, should be run as nearly as practicable under service conditions for a sufficient length of time to demonstrate that wiring, alignment, direction of rotation, speed range, commutation, rated output and operating characteristics are satisfactory.

(4)   All electrical devices and circuits also lighting, heating and galley equipment should be tested under operating conditions to verify that they are suitable and satisfactory for their purposes.

(5)   Each communicating system and alarm system should be thoroughly tested to determine its suitability and to verify its specified functioning.

(6)   Equipment installed to implement relevant Statutory requirements should be tested to ensure that all such requirements have been met. Where operation is required to be maintained from emergency sources of power, including automatic transfer of circuits to such emergency sources, correct functioning from and by such emergency supplies, should be tested and the duration of the emergency supplies where specified, should also be verified.

(7)   Communication equipment, navigational aids, depth-sounding, and broadcasting apparatus should be tested for the purpose of detecting interference from the electrical installation. If objectionable interference is found, it should be reduced by suitable means to the level prescribed in BS 1597.

(8)   The ventilation arrangements of vented type battery installations should be inspected to ensure that they are in accordance with 14.12. Ventilation air flow should be tested to confirm that at least the minimum quantity is obtained.

(9)   Attention is drawn to the special tests for propulsion equipment which are detailed in 25.10.

27.6   Where it is considered that the voltage at a consuming device may be unduly low, tests should be made to verify that the allowable voltage drop has not been exceeded. See also 11.4(4).

27.7   The appropriate ratings of fuses and the settings of adjustable protection devices and the full load current of the generators or cables protected should be indicated.

SECTION 28

DEFINITIONS AND EXPLANATIONS OF TERMS

Accessory

A device, other than current-using equipment, associated with such equipment or with the wiring of an installation.

Appropriate Authority

An 'Appropriate Authority' is a governmental body, a Classification Society or both, with whose Rules and Regulations a ship is required to comply.

Certified safe type of equipment

'Certified safe type of equipment' is electrical equipment or apparatus for use in a flammable atmosphere furnished with a certificate (recognised by the Appropriate Authority) which verifies that the equipment is suitable for use in the flammable atmosphere concerned.

Computer based system

A 'computer based system' consists of one or more programmable electronic devices with their connections, peripherals and software necessary to automatically carry out specified functions.

NOTE: The following type of programmable devices could form part of a computer system: main-frame, mini-computer, micro-computer, programmable logic controller.

Earthed system

An 'earthed system' is a system of distribution in which the neutral point or one conductor is normally connected to earth, which may be the general mass of the metal structure of the ship, in such a manner as will provide at all times an immediate discharge of electrical energy without danger.

Essential services

'Essential services' are those services essential for the safety of life and to the safe navigation and propulsion of a ship.

NOTE: In general, they will include auxiliary machinery necessary for propulsion and auxiliary power generation, bilge and fire pumping, essential deck machinery, engine and boiler room ventilation, navigation lights and essential lighting, steering gear, watertight doors, and such navigational aids, communication and alarm systems as may be required in an emergency or for safe operation of the ship.

Expert system

An 'expert system' is an intelligent knowledge based system that is designed to solve a problem using information that has been compiled from some form of human expertise.

Final circuit

A circuit connected directly to current-using equipment, or to a socket-outlet or socket-outlets or other outlet points for the connection of such equipment.

Fire resistant cables

Cables which maintain circuit integrity under fire conditions when tested to a recognised standard. Where such cables are required by Rules / Regulations of the Appropriate Authority the standards should be recognised by them.

Flameproof enclosure — Ex 'd'

Flameproof denotes an enclosure for electrical apparatus which will withstand an internal explosion of the flammable gas or vapour which may enter or which may originate inside the enclosure without suffering damage and without communicating the internal flame to the external flammable gas or vapour for which it is designed, through any joints or structural openings in the enclosure.

> NOTE 1   The term 'flameproof' is synonymous with the term 'explosionproof' as used in the USA for the class of apparatus dealt with in these Recommendations.

> NOTE 2   A flameproof enclosure in accordance with the foregoing definition will not necessarily or ordinarily be watertight, dust-tight or pressure-tight.

> NOTE 3   For further information see BS 5345, Parts 1 and 3.

Flame-retardant

A 'flame-retardant' material is one which having been ignited does not continue to burn, or burns for a very limited period, after the source of heat is removed, when subjected to the test requirements for 'self-extinguishing' materials specified in BS 476, Part 7.

A flame-retardant cable is one complying with the performance requirements of BS 4066, Part 1.

Hazardous area

A 'hazardous area' is an area in which explosive gas-air mixtures are, or may be expected to be, present in quantities such as to require special precautions for the construction and use of electrical apparatus.

Increased safety — Ex 'e'

A method of protection by which additional measures are applied to electrical apparatus to give increased security against the possibility of excessive temperatures and of the occurrence of arcs and sparks during the service life of the apparatus. It applies only to electrical apparatus, no parts of which produce sparks or arcs or exceed the limiting temperature in normal service.

NOTE: For further information see BS 5345, Parts 1 and 6.

Insulated system

An 'insulated system' is a system of distribution in which no point is normally connected to earth.

Intelligent knowledge based system

An 'intelligent knowledge based system' is a computer program which provides advice or makes decisions based on logical inference from a database of information.

Intrinsically safe — Ex 'i'

(i) Applied to a circuit, denotes that any electrical sparking that may occur in normal working and with the prescribed components, is incapable of causing an ignition of the prescribed flammable gas or vapour.

(ii) Applied to apparatus, denotes that it is so constructed that when installed and operated any electrical sparking that may occur in normal working, either in the apparatus or in the circuit associated therewith, is incapable of causing an ignition of the prescribed gas or vapour.

NOTE 1 The use of the term 'in normal working' is intended to cover sparking that may, in normal use, be produced by breaking line current, or a short-circuit across the lines, in the circuit that is required to be intrinsically safe. It is also intended to cover sparking that may be produced under conditions of fault.

NOTE 2 Apparatus of Category 'ia' is incapable of causing ignition in normal operation, or with a single fault, or with any combination of two faults applied. Apparatus of Category 'ib'

169

is incapable of causing ignition in normal operation, or with any single fault applied.

NOTE 3 Where part of the equipment is to be mounted outside the hazardous area or in a flameproof enclosure, assessment of intrinsic safety may be restricted to cover only such electrical sparking as may occur within the hazardous area or outside the flameproof enclosure.

NOTE 4 For further information see BS 5345, Parts 1 and 4.

Machinery spaces

'Machinery spaces' include all spaces used for propelling, auxiliary or refrigeration machinery, oil-filling stations and similar spaces, and trunks to such spaces.

Non-combustible material

'Non-combustible material' means material which when heated to a temperature of 750° C neither flames for longer than 10 seconds duration, nor raises either its internal temperature or the temperature of the test furnace more than 50° C above 750° C when tested in accordance with BS 476, Part 4.

Pressurized apparatus — Ex 'p'

Apparatus in which a protective gas is maintained at a pressure greater than that of the surrounding atmosphere.

Pressurized enclosure — Ex 'p'

The assembly of walls, surfaces or casings enclosing the electrical apparatus that serves to contain the protective gas.

NOTE 1 The pressurized enclosure may or may not be also the enclosure surrounding the live parts and ensuring the protection in other respects of the electrical apparatus.

NOTE 2 For further information on pressurization see BS 5345 Parts 1 and 5.

Residual current device

A mechanical switching device or association of devices intended to cause the opening of the contacts when the residual current attains a given value under specified conditions. See BS 4293.

Safety isolating transformer

A double wound transformer complying with BS 3535.

170

Software

'Software' is the program, procedures and associated documentation pertaining to the operation of a computer system and includes both application (user) program and the operating system (firmware) program.

Voltage, extra-low

A voltage which does not exceed 50 V a.c. r.m.s. between conductors, or between any conductor and earth, in a circuit isolated from the supply by means such as a safety isolating transformer or convertor with separate windings.

A voltage which does not exceed 50 V d.c. between conductors or any conductor and earth in a circuit isolated from higher voltage circuits.

Voltage, low

A "low voltage" is a voltage normally exceeding extra-low voltage but not exceeding 1000 V a.c. or 1500 V d.c. between conductors or 600 V a.c. or 900 V d.c. between conductors and earth.

Voltage, high

A "high voltage" is a voltage normally exceeding low voltage.

SECTION 29

GRAPHICAL SYMBOLS

It is desirable that drawings and instructions be prepared in accordance with the following British Standard, in so far as it applies:

> BS 3939: Guide for graphical symbols for electrical power, telecommunications and electronics diagrams.

Symbols additional to those given in British Standards should be based as far as possible on circuit elements depicted in the relevant Standards. Where doubt may otherwise arise, the use of simple circles or squares containing letters or numbers referring to an explanatory schedule is recommended.

APPENDIX A

LIST OF STANDARDS REFERRED TO IN TEXT

The Standards included in this Appendix are those referred to in the text of these Recommendations. In the applications of these Standards due allowance should be made where necessary for ambient temperature and the marine environment.

British Standards

Other British Standards may be applicable and are listed in the "British Standards Yearbook".

BS Numerical List

BS No.	Title	Clause
21	Pipe threads for tubes and fittings where pressure-tight joints are made on the threads	11.10(1)
88	Cartridge fuses for voltages up to and including 1000 V a.c. and 1500 V d.c.	8.13(1)
89	Direct acting indicating electrical measuring instruments and their accessories	6.9(1)
90	Direct acting electrical recording instruments and their accessories	6.9(1)
132	Steam turbines procurement	9.1(i)
159	Busbars and busbar connections	6.5
161	Tungsten filament lamps for general service (batch testing)	15.1
171	Power transformers	18.2, 18.3, Table 18.2
196	Protected-type non-reversible plugs, socket-outlets, cable-couplers and appliance-couplers with earthing contacts for single phase a.c. circuits up to 250 volts	19.4
229	Flameproof enclosure of electrical apparatus	1.31, 23.5(1) Note 1

173

174

BS No.	Title	Clause
3456	Safety of household and similar electrical appliances	16.1
Part 102 Section 102.25	Appliances for heating food by means of microwave energy	16.3
3535	Safety isolating transformers for industrial and domestic purposes	18.1 Note 2, Section 28
3676	Switches for domestic and similar purposes (for fixed or portable mounting)	19.3
3677	High pressure mercury vapour lamps	15.1
3772	Starters for fluorescent lamps	15.15
3863	Gas turbines procurement	9.1(ii)
3938	Current transformers	6.9(1)
3939	Graphical symbols for electric power, telecommunication and electronic diagrams	Section 29
3941	Voltage transformers	6.9(1)
4017	Capacitors for use in tubular fluorescent, high pressure mercury and low pressure sodium vapour discharge lamp circuits	15.15
4066	Tests on electric cables under fire conditions	10.1(5), 11.11(1), Section 28
4167	Electrically-heated catering equipment	16.1
4293	Residual current-operated circuit-breakers	16.20, Section 28, B.2(9) Note
4343	Industrial plugs, socket-outlets and couplers for a.c. and d.c. supplies	19.4
4417	Semiconductor rectifier equipments	17.1
4444	Guide to electrical earth monitoring	B.4(2)(i) Note

BS No.	Title	Clause
4533	Luminaires	15.1, 15.7, 15.9, 15.10
Part 102 Section 102.8	Handlamps	15.11(2)
4568	Steel conduit and fittings with metric threads of ISO form for electrical installations	11.10(1), 11.10(2), 11.10(5) Note
4579 Part 1	Performance of mechanical and compression joints in electric cable and wire connectors — compression joints in copper conductors	11.14(1)
4683	Electrical apparatus for explosive atmospheres	1.31, 23.5(1) Notes
4752 Part 1	Switchgear and controlgear for voltages up to and including 1000 V a.c. and 1200 V d.c. — Circuit-breakers	6.8(1), 8.3(1)(v)
4782	Ballasts for discharge lamps (excluding ballasts for tubular fluorescent lamps)	15.15
4941	Motor starters for voltages up to and including 1000 V a.c. and 1200 V d.c.	13.1
4944	Reactors, arc-suppression coils and earthing transformers for electric power systems	18.3
4999 Part 143 Part 144	Rotating electrical machines Specifications for tests Insulation of bars and coils of high voltage machines, including test methods	9.10 24.3(2)(ii)(b) 24.3(2)(i)
5042	Bayonet lampholders	15.2(5)
5227	AC metal-enclosed switchgear and control gear of rated voltages above 1 kV and up to and including 72.5 kV	13.1, 24.6(1)(i)
5260	Code of practice for radio interference suppression on marine installations	17.12 Note, 20.3, D.1, D.5(1)
5304	Code of practice. Safety of machinery	C3.4(5) Note
5308	Instrumentation cables	10.2

176

BS No.	Title	Clause
5311	High-voltage alternating-current circuit-breakers	24.6(2)(iii)
5345	Code of practice for the selection, installation and maintenace of electric apparatus for use in potentially explosive atmospheres (other than mining applications or explosive processing and manufacture)	1.38 Note 1, 23.2(1)(i), 23.3(1) Notes 1 & 2, Section 28
5424	Controlgear for voltages up to and including 1000 V a.c. and 1200 V d.c.	13.1
5467	Armoured cables with thermosetting insulation for electricity supply	10.2, 10.3, 11.17(4)
5486	Low-voltage switchgear and controlgear assemblies	6.2(1), 13.1
5490	Classification of degrees of protection provided by enclosures	1.17(2) Note, Table 1.1, 16.9
5501	Electrical apparatus for potentially explosive atmospheres	1.31, 16.23, 23.5(1) Note 1
5514	Reciprocating internal combustion engines: Performance	9.1(iii), 9.4(i)
5515	Code of practice for documentation of computer based systems	21.8(1)
5622	Guide for insulation co-ordination	24.3(3)
5655	Lifts and service lifts	13.8(1)
5856	Motor starters for voltages above 1 kV a.c. and 1.2 kV d.c.	13.1
5907	High voltage fuse-links for motor circuit applications	24.6(4)
5971	Safety of tungsten filament lamps for domestic and similar general lighting purposes	15.1
6004	PVC-insulated cables (non-armoured) for electric power and lighting	Table 2.1, Table 2.2, 10.2
6007	Rubber-insulated cables for electric power and lighting	11.17(7)

BS No.	Title	Clause
6141	Insulated cables and flexible cords for use in high temperature zones	6.4, 11.17(3), 13.1
6195	Insulated flexible cables and cords for coil leads	6.4, 13.1
6207	Mineral-insulated copper-sheathed cables with copper conductors	10.2
6231	PVC-insulated cables for switchgear and control gear wiring	6.4, 11.7(8), 13.1
6234	Polythene insulation and sheath of electric cables	Table 10.1
6346	PVC-insulated cables for electricity supply	10.2, 10.3, 11.17(4)
6351	Electric surface heating	16.16, 16.17
6360	Conductors in insulated cables and cords	10.1(2)
6387	Performance requirements for cables required to maintain circuit integrity under fire conditions	10.1(6)
6467	Electrical apparatus with protection by enclosure for use in the presence of combustible dusts	1.32
6500	Insulated flexible cords and cables	11.17(7), Table 12.19
6622	Cables with extruded cross-linked polyethylene or ethylene propylene rubber insulation for rated voltages from 3 800 / 6 600 V up to 19 000 / 33 000 V	10.3
6626	Code of practice for maintenance of electrical switchgear and control gear for voltages above 650 V and up to and including 36 kV	24.1(4) Note 2, 24.6(1)(iii)
6656	Guide to prevention of inadvertent ignition of flammable atmospheres by radio-frequency radiation	23.5(5)
6702	Lampholders for tubular fluorescent lamps and starterholders	15.3
6724	Armoured cables for electricity supply having thermosetting insulation with low emission of smoke and corrosive gases when affected by fire	10.2, 10.3, 11.5(1) Note 2

BS No.	Title	Clause
6746	PVC insulation and sheath of electric cables	Table 10.1, Tables 12.6, 12.8, 12.17, 12.18
6883	Elastomer-insulated cables for fixed wiring in ships	6.4, 10.2, 10.3, 11.17(8)
6899	Rubber insulation and sheath of electric cables	Table 10.1, 11.17(7)
6977	Insulated flexible cables for lifts and for other flexible connections	11.17(6)
7027	Limits and methods of measurement of the immunity of marine electrical and electronic equipment to conducted and radiated electromagnetic interference	20.4, 21.3(3)(iii), D.1

International Electrotechnical Commission Publications

IEC No.	Title	Clause
34-1	Rotating electrical machines — Part 1: Rating and performance	9.10
92 Series	Electrical installations in ships	
92-3	Cables (construction, testing and installations)	10.2, 11.17(4)
92-350	Low voltage shipboard power cables General construction and test requirements	10.2
93-351	Insulating material for shipboard power cables	Table 10.1, Tables 12.5, 12.7, 12.15, 12.16
92-353	Single and multicore cables with extruded solid insulation for voltages 0.6 / 1 kV	10.2
92-359	Sheathing materials for switchboard power and telecommunications cables	Table 10.1
92-374	Shipboard telecommunication cables and radio frequency cables. Telephone cables for non-essential communication services	10.2

APPENDIX B

GUIDANCE ON SOCKET-OUTLETS AND WELDING EQUIPMENT

B.1 General

(1) These notes give guidance on the choice of voltages and equipment for use with socket-outlets and on electric shock hazard in the use of electric arc welding equipment. See also Table 4.1.

(2) Compliance of the electrical installation, irrespective of its situation, with the recommendations of Section 2 is assumed.

B.2 Voltages for use with a.c. hand-held equipment (for welding purposes see B.5)

(1) Conditions vary to such an extent and are so difficult to define, that precise rules governing the application of appropriate voltages for portable equipment in various locations are not practicable. Furthermore the susceptibility of individuals to shock varies considerably. It is the purpose of this Appendix, however, to give guidance as to where particular voltages should be utilised.

(2) In dry areas of the accommodation spaces where the risk is not abnormal, supplies as in (4) of Table 4.1 are satisfactory for cabin fans, vacuum cleaners, table lamps etc. Additional safety, if considered necessary, can be obtained by using small local double wound isolating transformers in the manner provided for in 3(i) of Table 4.1.

(3) For supplies to electric shavers see 19.4(10).

(4) For handlamps 24 volts is recommended.

(5) In some circumstances a supply not exceeding 115 volts, obtained from a transformer of which the mid-point of the secondary (115 volts) winding is connected to earth, thus limiting the shock risk to earth to a maximum of 60 volts, may be appropriate.

(6) Hand-held tools can be obtained for 50 volts but current carrying difficulties can arise if lower voltages are chosen. If these supplies are derived from local isolating transformers limited to the supply of only one appliance, safety is further improved. Where a voltage of 50 volts or less is not practicable the alternatives given in Table 4.1(3) are acceptable. Adverse conditions occur, for example, due to water and spray on weather decks and low skin contact resistance as a result of humid conditions in tropical climates. These latter conditions can occur in any location, though they are less likely

181

to arise in the accommodation spaces, and supplies for such appliances as hand-held tools should therefore preferably not exceed 50 volts.

(7)   Where supplies are provided under the terms of item 3(i) of Table 4.1, experience indicates that the loading of each isolated secondary circuit should be limited to 5 kVA and should supply only one socket outlet.

(8)   Under particular conditions any a.c. voltage even as low as 50 volts can be fatal. Even lower voltages can cause injury due to being thrown off balance by a shock. Very adverse conditions occur where personnel and equipment can become damp while surrounded by conductive surfaces, particularly in restricted spaces and the use of lower voltage equipment is recommended in these circumstances. Where this is impracticable, the recommendations of B.2(9) or B.4(2)(i) should additionally be followed.

(9)   For circuits having adequate earth return path (i.e. one point of the supply is connected to earth) the use of residual current devices (RCD) in addition to other precautions is recommended.

NOTE: Reference is made to BS 4293. Particular attention is drawn to the need to select a RCD which is resistant to the marine environment e.g. vibration, salt atmosphere, etc. Residual current operated circuit breakers of the type specified in BS 4293 were formerly known as high sensitivity current operated earth leakage circuit-breakers (ELCB).

B.3   Choice of hand-held equipment (for welding purposes see B.5)

Careful consideration should be given to the selection of hand-held equipment to ensure that it is suitable for the conditions of use on board ship. Many devices that may be entirely suitable for use ashore may not be adequately designed and constructed to meet marine requirements, particularly temperature, salt laden atmosphere, etc, see Section 1. Because of the risk of tracking across insulation the use of Class I appliances, in preference to Class II, is recommended unless the appliance is solely for use in dry areas of accommodation.

NOTE: Class I appliances are provided with facilities for earthing non-current carrying parts. Class II appliances have double insulation and / or reinforced insulation throughout and are without provision for earthing.

B.4   Voltages for use with a.c. portable and transportable equipment

(1)   The recommendations for hand-held equipment in B.2 should be followed as far as practicable.

(2)   It is recognised, however, that the limits of voltage given are not always practicable for equipment such as submersible pumps, deck scalers, refrigerated containers etc. In these cases, where three phase supplies up to 500 volts may be involved, the additional precautions in (i) and (ii) of this sub-clause or a combination are recommended.

182

(i)   Circuits which monitor the continuity of the earth connections and automatically disconnect the supply on loss of earth continuity. This arrangement will not, however, be effective when double insulated or all insulated equipment is used since such equipment has no provision for an earth connection.

NOTE: Reference is made to BS 4444

(ii)   Each socket-outlet or group of socket-outlets supplied through a RCD. For this method to be effective the supply must be earthed at one point. In ships with unearthed systems double wound isolating transformers with one point of the secondary winding solidly earthed should be used. See also NOTE to Clause B.2(9).

B.5   Electric shock hazard in the use of electric arc welding equipment

(1)   The risk from electric shock in the use of electric arc welding equipment in certain special locations, for example, as described in B.2(8), is not always appreciated.

(2)   Since the effect of shock from direct current is less (at the operating voltages used) than with alternating current, the use of welding sets having a d.c. output, especially those incorporating d.c. generators providing an open circuit (idling) voltage of 70 volts or less, is recommended. Direct current obtained from rectified alternating current may, however, contain a degree of a.c. ripple which is excessive and would greatly reduce the advantage provided by pure direct current in which case it is recommended that the idling voltage be limited to 42 volts by provision of voltage reduction safety devices.

(3)   Voltage reduction safety devices which limit the "idling" voltage to 25 volts or less are also available for use with alternating current electric arc welding plant.

(4)   These safety devices are intended to ensure that the idling voltage only is applied until there is contact between the electrode and the "work" when the full open circuit voltage becomes available to strike the arc. Once struck, welding continues in the normal way at the voltage necessary to maintain the arc (normally 25-30 volts) until the arc is broken.

(5)   Electrode holders should be of the fully insulated type.

(6)   When joints in the cables are necessary, the connectors should also be fully insulated and should be designed and used so that live parts are not exposed when disconnected. A "go and return" system where two cables are used from the welding set with one cable solidly clamped to the workpiece is recommended in all cases.

(7)   Means should be available whereby the current can rapidly be cut off from the electrode holder should the operator get into difficulties. Means of

disconnection should be available to the welder for use when changing electrodes.

(8)   Attention is drawn to Merchant Shipping Notice No. M752, issued by the Department of Transport Marine Directorate, which gives operational information on the use of electric arc welding.

APPENDIX C

GUIDANCE
ON THE TREATMENT
OF THE NEUTRAL POINT

Table C.1 Summary of principal features of the neutral earthing methods

Means of earthing	INTENTIONALLY EARTHED NEUTRAL SYSTEMS						
	High Reactance "Petersen"	Not Intentionally Earthed Systems "Unearthed" "Isolated"	High Resistance	Low Reactance	Low Resistance	Solid Connection
System voltage	All methods are potentially applicable (but note higher voltage systems are likely to have higher V/A earth fault levels which may make solid, or low impedance methods, unattractive)					
Overvoltages	The most significant overvoltages are due to causes not influenced by the method of neutral earthing					
Electric shock risk	All major installations are potentially lethal whatever method of neutral earthing is used					
Use of RCD for electrical safety	←—— See NOTE 1 of Clause C.3.2 ——→					Acceptable
Use of 3-phase 4-wire supply	←—— Not Acceptable ——→					Acceptable
Earth fault current magnitude	Theoretically may be zero	Depends on system capacitance but usually very low, say 1A	Usually less than 20 A. Can approach unearthed value	←—— Typically 200-400 A ——→		May be up to 50% greater than symmetrical 3-phase value
Sustained operation with earth fault	Possible	Normally possible	May be possible but not advisable	←—————— Not possible ——————→		

186

Minimum earth fault protection required	Alarm or Indication	Alarm or Indication	From Alarm/ Indication to earth fault relay	From earth fault relay to overcurrent protection	Overcurrent protection
Switchgear fault rating	Can be rated on normal phase-to-phase or 3-phase symmetrical fault value →				May have to be rated on single phase-to-earth, or phase-to phase-to-earth value
Earth fault location	Faults not self revealing and must normally be located manually unless core balance CTs are fitted		If relays fitted, faults self revealing. Otherwise must be located manually	Faults self revealing by overcurrent or relay operation	Faults are self revealing on overcurrent
Fire risk	Negligible	Very low provided that earth fault current does not exceed 1 A. Prolonged fault may present a hazard		Risk of arc igniting flammable gases. High impedance faults can lead to burning at fault location	
Flash hazard (phase–to–earth)	Low ————	———— Increasing ————		————	High
Availability of suitable equipment	Similar generation & distribution equipment is applicable on all systems ←				Allows use of land-based lighting and hotel services equipment

NOTE: In the spectrum of possible neutral earthing impedance magnitudes the 'Not Intentionally Earthed' values are not the highest.

187

C.1   Introduction

(1)   Whether or not to intentionally earth the neutral point in marine electrical power systems has been subject to debate ever since a.c. generation and distribution systems were introduced into ships. The continuing debate suggests that there is no single 'best' method, therefore, guidance would be helpful to designers in selecting a method for a particular application.

(2)   Although extensive literature exists on the subject of treating the neutral points ('neutral earthing'), little of it deals specifically with marine installations, and the material that is available reflects the range of views upon which systems are most suitable for given applications.

(3)   The report 'Neutral Earthing of Marine Electrical Power Systems' a study commissioned by the Department of Trade contains a bibliography and is recommended as a comprehensive source of reference. The report, Reference No. YM3889A/82, is available from YARD Consulting Engineers, Charing Cross Tower, ·Glasgow, U.K. G2 4PP.

C.2   Methods of treating the neutral point in electrical systems

C.2.1   The neutral point

The neutral point of a healthy balanced, steady state three phase voltage system is defined as the geometric centre of the equilateral voltage vector triangle. In star connected machinery the neutral can be made physically available (for the supply of single phase loads for instance), but in systems with delta connected supplies the neutral point is an artefact and can only be made available by the use of a star connected earthing device.

C.2.2   The neutral point under fault conditions

Under fault conditions the equilateral voltage vector triangle becomes distorted and transient asymmetrical voltages arise. For given types of fault on a system the transient voltages and fault currents are influenced by:

— the impedance between the neutral point and earth;
— the characteristics of the system in question;

and these are considered in the following clauses.

C.2.3   Neutral earthing methods

(1)   On occurrence of a fault from line to earth, the steady state and transient voltages to earth and fault currents vary with the impedance between the neutral point and earth. This impedance is dependent on the treatment of the neutral point and the following methods of intentionally earthing the neutral are available:

188

— high reactance (also referred to as 'Petersen' or 'resonant');
— high resistance;
— low reactance;
— low resistance;
— solid connection.

(2)   Although not intentionally connected to earth, the so called 'unearthed' or 'isolated' system is in fact capacitively earthed by the distributed capacitance to earth of the phase conductors throughout the system together with any interference suppression capacitors.

(3)   The principal features of these methods are presented in Table C.1.

C.2.4   Marine electrical systems

(1)   Marine electrical systems have a number of significant characteristics which differentiate them from typical land based systems. These need to be borne in mind when considering neutral earthing of marine systems.

(2)   The zero and positive sequence impedance of a.c. generators, which are the usual sources of power, are such that line to neutral fault current can significantly exceed the symmetrical three phase fault value. This is of importance to the rating of switchgear and to potential damage to the core of a generator following an internal fault.

(3)   The interconnection of the neutral points of generators, particularly those of different sizes or different winding configurations, or even identical generators with different loadings, can give rise to undesirable circulating harmonic currents, especially third harmonic currents.

(4)   Distribution circuits are geographically compact and distribution is by cable. The proximity of the cables to the hull structure and also of machine windings to earthed stator cores unavoidably gives rise to significant phase to earth capacitance. Typical values lie in the range 1 to 5 microfarads per phase and this can increase appreciably if interference suppression capacitors are used extensively.

(5)   Fault power factors are low with the result that the ratio of peak asymmetrical current to r.m.s. symmetrical current is high and tends to the maximum ratio of $2\sqrt{2} : 1$.

(6)   System natural resonant frequences are high, typically 5-10 kHz. At these frequencies, the oscillatory circuit is usually over damped with the result that oscillatory overvoltages are unlikely to occur.

(7)   Earth return impedances are low due to the metal structure.

(8)   The wet, salty, high vibration level operating environment is harsh and may cause earth faults to occur, particularly in exposed electrical fittings.

(9)   Because comprehensive spares may not be carried on board and maintenance personnel may not be sufficiently specialised, the diagnosis of faults and their subsequent repair may not be undertaken until return to port.

C.3   Selection of neutral earthing method

C.3.1   General

(1)   In view of the wide variety of types and sizes of ships and their associated electrical installations there is no single 'best' method for treating the neutral point in marine electrical power systems. Good, safe, correctly engineered installations can be achieved in a number of ways and so each application should be considered and designed on its merits.

(2)   In order to select a method for a given application, a careful assessment should be made of the relative importance of all technical, operational and commercial factors, see Table C.1.
Subjective judgements are mostly unavoidable, but the following considerations should be appreciated when making this assessment:

(i)   factors not significant to selection of neutral earthing method;
(ii)   factors significant to selection of neutral earthing method;
(iii) applicability of neutral earthing methods to marine electrical systems.

C.3.2   Factors not significant

(1)   Although important in their own right, certain factors apply equally however the neutral point is treated and so can be discounted when selecting between methods.

(2)   Electric shock — phase to earth

The treatment of the neutral point of the electrical power system has no significant effect on shock risk to personnel. This is because the human tolerance to shock currents is so low that any method of earthing the neutral has the possibility of allowing a potentially lethal current to flow. Even the line to earth capacitive current in unearthed distribution power systems could permit a dangerous current to flow.

NOTE 1   On sub-circuits having a nominal voltage not greater than 660 V, protection against harmful phase to earth shocks can be achieved by means of a residual current device (RCD).
This RCD should be of high sensitivity having a residual operating current not exceeding 30 mA and an operating time not exceeding 30 ms at a residual current of 150 mA. RCDs can only be effective on solidly earthed sub-systems and so a transformer with earthed secondary windings should be fitted if RCDs are to be used on unearthed systems.

190

NOTE 2   On sub-circuits having a nominal voltage not greater than 240 V, protection against harmful phase to earth shocks may be achieved by means of isolating transformers.

NOTE 3   Further guidance for protection against electric shock is given in Appendix B.

(3)   Overvoltages

The largest and, therefore, most significant overvoltages on marine systems are produced by switching surges, which are independent of the method of treatment of the neutral.

NOTE: The significant system overvoltage that is influenced by the method of system neutral earthing is that caused by the 'intermittent earth fault'. This can occur on unearthed neutral systems if the arc associated with an earth fault extinguishes and restrikes producing overvoltages at the natural frequency of the system. In marine systems, typical natural frequencies are several kilohertz and system losses are such that these frequencies are normally over damped hence the associated overvoltages do not occur. Guidance on calculating whether damping in a system is critical is given in C.5.

(4)   System voltage

System voltage itself is not a determining factor in selecting a neutral earthing method. Satisfactory installations of all types can be engineered at all voltages given in Sections 4 and 24.

C.3.3   Significant factors

(1)   Earth faults

(i)   Improvements generally to insulating systems and standards make earth faults less likely to occur, but they are still the most common fault.

(ii)   The majority of earth faults occur in miscellaneous electrical equipment away from the principal power production and distribution systems (e.g. in luminaires, galley, deck fittings, etc.) rather than in switchboards or important motors. There are, therefore, advantages in isolating such equipment or arranging for the faults to be self clearing.

(iii)   In three phase circuits, single phase-to-earth faults are likely to escalate into phase-to-phase faults unless steps are taken to reduce this possibility (e.g. by use of phase segregation barriers). This is particularly so for low impedance neutral earthing methods.

(iv)   The occurrence of a solid earth fault on a high impedance or unearthed neutral system will increase the phase-to-earth voltage

191

stress on the two healthy phases for the duration of the fault. This power frequency overvoltage will not damage equipment in the short term, however, manufacturers have different definitions of the length of time for which this can be tolerated.

(2)   Continuity of supply

Continuity of supply following a single earth fault is an important argument in favour of the unearthed and high impedance methods, but for it to be a valid one, the earth fault must be such that it would have caused the loss of supply to an essential service. This requires that:

— the earth fault must occur in the essential service itself or in its associated distribution or control circuits;
— the electrical system must be earth fault free at the time the earth fault occurs on the essential service;
— the earth fault does not escalate into a phase-to-phase fault which causes the loss of the essential service anyway;
— the essential service is not backed up in some other reliable way, e.g. standby supply or unit.

(3)   Switchgear rating

The most onerous duty for switchgear in a marine system is dependent upon machine and distribution parameters and will normally be a phase to phase or three phase symmetrical fault. However, with the low impedance neutral earthing methods the phase-to-earth, or phase-to-phase-to-earth fault current can exceed the three phase fault current and so can become the specifying parameter for the switchgear.

(4)   Availability of suitable electrical equipment

The availability of suitable electrical equipment is not a significant factor for generation and primary distribution equipment because the equipment is similar for both earthed or unearthed systems. However at sub-circuit level unearthed systems require special fittings (e.g. two pole switches, non-standard voltages, etc.). Many commercial fittings designed for use ashore on solid earthed neutral systems are available but are only single police devices. This must favour the use of 380 V or 415 V, 3-phase 4-wire systems for lighting and hotel services.

(5)   Fault location

(i)   In solidly earthed neutral systems, faults are self clearing either by fuse or circuit-breaker action;
(ii)   In high impedance systems fault location is either:

— expensive, if special fault locating equipment is fitted or;
— laborious and time consuming if the fault is traced by successive isolation of suspect circuits.

In the long term this fault finding procedure can be more disruptive to the

192

power system than that associated with automatic fault isolation systems, because the total power availability may be reduced.

(6)   Fire risk

(i)   Fire risk arises in two ways:
        (a)   burning at the point of fault;
        (b)   ignition of flammable materials or gases by a fault arc.

(ii)   The risk of burning depends upon the magnitude and duration of the fault current and is, therefore, higher in the solid or low impedance neutral earthed systems, unless earth fault protection is specifically provided by some more sensitive means than overcurrent protection. The ignition hazard is potentially serious in tankers, etc., and every effort should be made to minimise prospective current flow through hazardous areas.

(7)   Flash hazard

A flash hazard arises when a fault occurs in close proximity to individuals. For interphase faults the hazard is the same for all types of neutral earthing. For single phase-to-earth faults the hazard is greatest with solid earthing and reduces with increasing neutral earthing impedance.

C.3.4   Applicability to marine electrical systems

(1)   Unearthed neutral systems

(i)   Unearthed neutral systems are acceptable for generation and distribution systems of any size. The principal advantages are:

        — an earth fault can occur on an essential service without causing loss of supply to that service;
        — the otherwise adverse effects of the low zero sequence impedance of the generators on the fault capacity of the switchgear is avoided;
        — there is no need for any neutral connection, thus neutral switching and circulating currents are avoided;
        — earth fault protection costs are low;
        — fire and flash hazards are low;
        — small, isolated, unearthed low voltage sub-systems can be inherently safe since the potential earth fault current can be restricted to less than the lethal level.

(ii)   The principal disadvantage is that fault location is a time consuming, tedious manual task, but one which should be carried out quickly to avoid jeopardising the integrity of supply to essential services should a second fault occur. For this reason it is preferable not to use unearthed supplies for loads prone to earth faults.

(2)   High reactance earthed neutral systems

The high reactance 'Petersen' method is rarely worth considering unless:

— the system capacitive currents are high (e.g. where large numbers of interference suppression capacitors are used);
— there is a paramount need to limit the earth fault current.

(3)   High resistance earthed neutral systems

(i) The high resistance earthed approach is often advocated to control overvoltages, but this is not usually relevant in marine systems.

NOTE: Under solid earth fault conditions, a 4-wire system supplying single phase loads can develop significant phase to neutral power frequency overvoltages which could be hazardous.

(ii) It is possible to limit the earth fault current to a level that allows continued operations with a single fault on the system but the resulting fault current, and hence fire risk, is of necessity larger that it would otherwise have been with the system operated unearthed. The method does allow earth fault relays to be used.

(4)   Low resistance or low reactance earthed neutral systems

It is only worthwhile considering these low impedance methods if it is desired to obtain the benefits of the solidly earthed approach but the resulting earth fault current would be too high. Low reactance is preferable to low resistance because it is cheaper for a given rating and will offer greater impedance to third harmonic circulating currents, while giving minimum volt drop at fundamental frequency.

(5)   Solidly earthed neutral systems

(i) The solidly earthed system is especially useful for supplying sub circuits prone to earth faults;
(ii) At low voltage, 4-wire solidly earthed systems have the advantage o better economy and automatic fault location for the supply of singl phase loads;
(iii) In large systems where power is generated at a high voltage transformers are automatically required. This creates the opportunit' to use 4-wire solidly earthed sub-systems;
(iv) In ships in which generation can satisfactorily be carried out at 380 ' or 415 V, 3-phase 4-wire solidly earthed systems can also be used thu enabling control and lighting to be supplied without specia transformers. For this to be acceptable, the continuity of suppl argument needs specific attention together with the effects of paralle generators and third harmonic currents.

194

NOTE: To ensure that they do not fail to danger, control circuits should be solidly earthed in one pole and fused in the second pole, see BS 5304.

C.4   Good practice for the selected neutral earthing method

C.4.1   General

(1)   The treatment of the neutral of a particular installation will depend on the relative importance of the factors discussed in this Appendix.

(2)   Where different voltage levels or different types of service are involved, the neutral treatment should be dealt with for each part regardless of the other parts.

(3)   Once a particular method of neutral earthing has been selected for all or part of a system, attention should be given to the topics listed under the respective method.

C.4.2   Unearthed neutral systems

(1)   To avoid jeopardising the main power system through sub-circuit earth faults, consider the use of localised earthed systems for supplying lighting and hotel services.

(2)   At the design stage, consider what actions can be taken to ease the fault location process by, for example:

— adequate cable spacing may facilitate the use of fault locating equipment;
— provision of a "fault making switch" which could be used at a convenient time to temporarily connect the system neutral to earth and thus cause the faulty circuit to be self revealing by operation of its overcurrent protection.

NOTE: It may be necessary to use a suitable impedance in series with the switch to limit the earth fault current to the phase-to-phase or three phase symmetrical value.

(3)   Estimate the system capacitance fault current at the design stage and then measure it to ensure that the fire hazard is not unacceptable.

(4)   Assess the benefits offered by phase segregation barriers to reduce the likelihood of earth faults becoming phase faults.

(5)   Fit double pole switches.

(6)   Alert the operating staff to the need to remove earth faults as quickly as possibly by specifying that a warning notice should be installed adjacent to the earth fault indication lamps.

C.4.3   Earthed neutral systems

(1)   General

(i)   Avoid use of neutral switching arrangements by connecting each generator to earth.

(ii)   Where earth fault relays are used, carry out primary and secondary injection tests and record results for comparison with results taken subsequently.

(2)   Solidly earthed neutral

(i)   If generator neutrals are solidly connected, special attention should be paid to circulating harmonic currents.

(ii)   Discrimination should be achieved under earth fault conditions.

(iii)   The switchgear rating should be adequate for the earth fault current duty.

(iv)   Phase to neutral supplies should be switched in the live pole.

(v)   Single phase loads should be balanced between the phases as far as possible.

(vi)   As far as is practicable, single phase socket-outlets from different phases should not be installed within a single compartment.

(vii)   Inspections should be carried out regularly to check the integrity of the neutral earth connection to the ship's structure.

C.5   Calculation for damping of oscillatory overvoltages

C.5.1   Basis

The interconnected generators, motors and cables have distributed inductances and capacitances which combine to form a resonant circuit. Oscillations which occur in this circuit are damped out by the various losses that occur in cables, machine windings, damper bars, etc. If the damping is sufficient, overvoltages cannot build up.

C.5.2   Procedure

(1)   For each combination of generators, motors, cable lengths, etc, produce an equivalent R-L-C circuit and calculate its natural frequency, f_o, by the following formula:

$$f_o = \frac{1}{2\pi \sqrt{LC}}$$

NOTE: When one phase is faulted to earth, the distributed phase to earth capacitance of that phase is short-circuited hence producing a modified equivalent circuit. Thus, there are two frequencies for each circuit combination, one for when the fault is made and one for when it is broken.

196

(2)   Establish the sources of loss in the circuit and convert to an equivalent resistance 'R_e' as follows, noting that the losses must be obtained at the natural frequency of the system:

- — for cables, use manufacturers' data on effective resistance per unit length at the frequency concerned;
- — for machine and transformer winding losses, use the eddy losses at rated current;
- — for machine and transformer iron losses, calculate the losses at the appropriate frequency assuming rated volts.

(3)   Check for damping

(i)   If R_e is greater than twice $\sqrt{L/C}$, the circuit is critically damped and resonant oscillations cannot be sustained.

(ii)   If R_e is smaller than twice $\sqrt{L/C}$, damped oscillations will occur. However, if the time constant of the decay of these oscillations ($t = L/R_e$) is small compared to the period of restriking of the arcing facing (i.e. mains frequency), overvoltages cannot build up.

APPENDIX D

GUIDANCE ON ELECTROMAGNETIC COMPATIBILITY

D.1   Introduction

The developing use of electric / electronic equipment of all types has greatly increased the likelihood of electromagnetic interference (EMI) between one device and another. Where certain classes of equipment are involved, safety could be affected.

Hitherto most cases of such interference appear to have been treated on an *ad hoc* basis after the equipment has already been installed and in operation. However as the number and sophistication of equipment fitted increases, the successful achievement of such piecemeal remedies is likely to prove increasingly difficult. It is becoming essential therefore, for steps to be taken in the design and construction, ideally at the drawing board stage, to ensure that an overall electromagnetically compatible installation will be achieved.

Note has to be taken therefore of the possible susceptibility to interference of each piece of electrical equipment and its own propensity for causing interference. The maximum degree of electric coupling that can be permitted between the various units, interconnecting cables, etc, has to be estimated to ensure that an acceptable electromagnetic environment can be achieved.

To realise a fully compatible installation it is necessary, ideally, to have complete quantitative data on all the above aspects. This is generally not available at the present time. Nevertheless, great improvements can be achieved by the adoption of general design techniques that will give inherent protection against interference. This Appendix outlines various measures that should contribute significantly towards this and gives information on general installation practices, screening, separation of cables, etc., that have shown themselves to be very successful in reducing the effects of stray coupling between units of equipment.

Much published information exists. The bibliography commissioned by the Department of Industry, 'Bibliography of References to Electromagnetic Compatibility Aboard Ships', is recommended as a comprehensive source of reference. The Bibliography is contained in YARD Memorandum No. YM 3634A/81 and is available from YARD Consulting Engineers, Charing Cross Tower, Glasgow, U.K. G2 4PP.

Reference can also be made to BS 1597, BS 5260, BS 7207 and IEC 533.

D.2   Types of interference

Interference energy may be propagated from its source to the affected equipment by one or both of the following:

(i)   Conducted interference, i.e. by conduction along power supply and / or other cables connecting the source to the apparatus.

(ii) Radiated interference, i.e. by direct radiation from the source and its immediate associated cabling into the affected apparatus and its immediate associated wiring.

Either type can be considered as narrowband or broadband although these terms are somewhat subjective. Historically, they have been used to describe the situation where the interference spectrum is less than or greater than the bandwidth of a specified interference measuring receiver. With the increasing use of electronic equipment with a wide frequency acceptance bandwidth they tend to be used in a different way, and the interference is described as narrow or broadband with reference to the particular equipment. For example an interference signal with a 1 MHz spectrum will appear as a narrow band signal to an equipment with a bandwidth of 10 MHz and as a broadband signal to an equipment with a bandwidth of 1 kHz.

D.3 Modes of interference propagation and coupling to interference sources

(1) Conducted interference

Two modes of propagation are possible for conducted interference:

(i) Symmetric or differential mode on which the interference energy is propagated between the 'go' and the 'return' lines of the connecting cable.
(ii) Asymmetric or common mode in which the interference energy is propagated between one or both of the 'go' and 'return' lines and earth. In practice this mode is the more significant because the area of the magnetic loop so formed is much greater than that formed in the symmetric mode.

(2) Types of mutual coupling

Coupling between circuits may be inductive, capacitive or resistive or a combination of these:

(i) Inductive coupling — this is the predominant coupling mode in high current, low frequency installations.
(ii) Capacitive coupling — this is the predominant coupling mode in low current, high impedance installations. Capacitive coupling is particularly important at high frequencies due to the low effective value of capacitive coupling impedances.
(iii) Resistive coupling — this coupling exists between equipments which share a common resistive path.

(3) Coupling effects of earth currents

Interference can be coupled into cables near a nominal earth plane if the latter carries significant localised interference currents. Such situations need to be avoided in installations where the structure / hull and superstructure,

199

handrails, stays, etc, may effectively form part of the earth return system. Possible causes which need to be considered include:

- cathodic protection systems;
- earth leakage current from high voltage systems;
- earth current from capacitors used for interference suppression;
- power-factor correction;
- radio frequency (RF) currents due to the structure / hull acting as a return path for the radio transmitting system;
- the structure / hull acting as a receiving antenna for externally radiated fields.
- use of arc welding equipment.

D.4 Installation practice designed to reduce interference transmission and pick-up

(1) General considerations

In the early planning of the installation of equipment it is essential that electromagnetic compatibility (EMC) is given serious consideration and the following guidelines should be adopted when setting up an EMC control plan.

(i) The EMC characteristics / requirements of each equipment to be installed should be obtained.

(ii) Equipments likely to produce EMI should not be installed in the same compartment as equipment which is EMI sensitive without taking adequate precautions, i.e. by additional local shielding and / or filtering.

(iii) It is highly desirable that sensitive low power equipment such as radio receivers are contained in a fully screened compartment to exclude or reduce their susceptibility to interfering fields. High power equipments likely to generate high interfering fields, e.g. radio transmitters and transceivers, may be installed in separate compartments to reduce radiation but do not necessarily require the same degree of screening. Care should be taken to ensure that transmitter remote control units, when installed alongside interference susceptible equipments, are adequately isolated for EMI from their associated transmitters.

(iv) All radiating cables and those carrying signals likely to be affected by interference should be separated in accordance with D.4(2) and, where necessary, protected by screening and / or filtering.

(v) Such cables should be identified in accordance with D.4(3). Antenna positioning should take into account the provisions of D.5.

(2) Separation

Separation of cables to reduce mutual coupling should be an important consideration in the design of an electromagnetic compatible installation. Until more specific testing has been carried out one of the following alternative methods is recommended. Where it is not possible to meet these

200

guidelines other means to reduce coupling e.g. screened trunking or twisted pairs should be considered.

(i) (a) Mains cables (Cable class A), should not be grouped with sensitive cables.

(b) Radio receiver feeders (Cable class B), may be grouped together but should be separated from all other cables by at least 50 mm and at least 75 mm from fluorescent tubes.

(c) Radio transmitter feeders (Cable class C), may be grouped together but should be separated from all other cables by at least 100 mm. As far as possible they should also be routed away from sensitive equipments. Where it might be difficult to achieve an adequate separation it may be necessary to take special precautions such as enclosing the cables in screened trunking.

(d) Small pulse cables, digital-data cables and databus cables (Cable class D), should be separated from all other cables by at least 50 mm and from fluorescent tubes by at least 75 mm. Preferably these cables should be run separately from each other also by at least 50 mm.

(e) Remote teleprinter terminal cables (Cable class E), should be run throughout their length in metal conduit which should be separated from all other cables by at least 50 mm.

(f) Crossovers, where made at right angles, may have the separation distance at the crossover reduced by 75% of the foregoing values.

(g) Table D.1 summarises the minimum distance in millimetres between cables which have been classed A to E.

Table D.1 Minimum distance in millimetres between cables which have been classed A to E

Cable class	A	B	C	D	E*
A	—	75+	100	75	50
B	75	—	100	50	50
C	100	100	—	100	100
D	75	50	100	50	50
E*	50	50	100	50	50

* Cables in metallic conduit

(ii) (a) The alternative approach to the cable spacing is to grade cables into four categories:

201

1 — interfering cables, e.g. power cables supplying non-linear loads,etc;
2 — non-interfering and non-susceptible cables;
3 — interfering and susceptible cables, e.g. digital signal;
4 — susceptible cables, e.g. analogue cables supplying low level signals.

(b) Multicore cables should be graded taking account of worst case circumstances. All cables of the same grade should be run together and separated from other grades by the minimum distances given in Table D.2.

Table D.2 Minimum distance in millimetres between cables which have been graded 1 to 4

Grade	Grade	Minimum distance
1	4	300
1	2	100
2	3	100
3	4	100

(3)   Identification

In order to ensure that both initial installations and retro-fit cabling achieves an acceptable EMC standard such cables should be identified in a permanent fashion after installation by colour banding or painting at the ends and, as far as practicable, when entering or leaving compartments. The following convention is recommended, but care is necessary to ensure that no confusion is caused with other colour coding schemes which may also be in use. It is recommended that explanatory notices drawing attention to the colours being used should be displayed in all locations especially where confusion between systems may arise.

(i)   Cables which may emit EMI and which may be run together but must be separated from all other cables by at least 100 mm. COLOUR CODE — V.

(ii)   Cables which may emit EMI but which must not be run together and must be separated from all other cables by at least 100 mm and from fluorescent lamps by at least 75 mm. COLOUR CODE — W.

(iii)   Cables which carry pulses in excess of 100 W peak which may not be run together and must be separated from all other cables by at least 300 mm. COLOUR CODE — X. See also D.5(5)(ii).

(iv)   Cables which are susceptible to EMI and may be run together but must be separated from all other cables by at least 50 mm and from fluorescent lamps by at least 75 mm. COLOUR CODE — Y.

202

(v)   Cables which are susceptible to EMI and must not be run together and must be separated from all other cables by at least 50 mm and from fluorescent lamps by at least 75 mm. COLOUR CODE — Z.

(4)   Screening compartments

Where compartments are required to exclude or confine EMI the construction should meet the following requirements:

(i)   The d.c. resistance between any two points on the compartment shell, or between the compartment and main structure, should be not greater than 0.01 ohms. Non-conducting housings, e.g. plastic, require to be coated by a continuous conducting layer e.g. metal foil, preferably during manufacture.

(ii)   All metallic conduits, pipes, cable screens, etc., should be bonded at their point of entry to the compartment preferably by a bonding gland giving circumferential contact.

    If a "pigtail" bond has to be used it is essential for it to be of the absolute shortest length and connected to the compartment at the point of entry of the pipe, etc.

(iii)   Where the performance of a pipe system, e.g. water pipes with thermal lagging, could be impaired by the presence of an electrical bond other means such as the enclosure of the pipe in a screened trunking and RF sealed at the points of exit and entry should be considered.

(iv)   All external doors, windows (gauze covered or otherwise opaque to RF), hatches, inspection plates should be RF sealed by a continuous bond around their perimeter.

(v)   A continuous bond is one where good electrical contact is achieved throughout its length. Such a bond may be achieved by the use of copper or bronze "weatherstrip".

(vi)   All power supply cables entering and terminating in a screened compartment which are not bonded at the point of entry, should pass through an appropriate EMI filter at that point.

(5)   Screening of cables and connectors

(i)   All receiving antenna feeders should be screened throughout their length. Coaxial cables are normally used for this type of feeder.

(ii)   Other cables carrying sensitive currents and in particular those connected to the output terminals of attentuation filters should be screened by the use of screened cable or by continuous welded conduit electrically bonded across the joints between sections.

(iii)   Where screened cable runs are longer than three metres and / or carry very sensitive signals, it may be necessary to consider more effective means such as double screened cables, or solid drawn metallic conduit.

(iv)   Screwed or clip-on connectors should be used with discretion, since the inefficient screening of the connector assembly can nullify the efforts spent in screening interconnecting cables.

203

(6)   Earthing and bonding

(i)   Each unit of radio / electrical equipment should have its own individual earth taken to the structure.
(ii)   The use of busbar earthing arrangements should be avoided.
(iii)   The earthing strap should be solid, as short as practicable and of low inductance. It should be assembled using washers of diameter equal to the width of the strap using suitable lock nuts; the whole assembly to provide a d.c. resistance of less than 0.01 ohms. After a d.c. resistance check the whole assembly should be painted or otherwise preserved against corrosion. The use of a conductive paste smeared on all contact faces will help to ensure a lasting low resistance contact.
(iv)   The earth strap should not be attached to the equipment using any of the bolts, or other parts, of shock or anti-vibration mountings.
(v)   Choice of bonding materials
        Where the metallic composition of the equipment differs from that of the structure, care should be taken in the selection of the bonding strap to minimise possible ill effects of contact potentials.
        Corrosion at one or both interfaces can render the bond ineffective in a short time. The bonding strap should ideally be compatible with both metals.
        Bonding strap materials which are considered suitable are copper or aluminium, see Table D.3. In the case of the latter, it is essential to ensure that the contact surfaces are oxide free, and that they are coated with a thin layer of conducting paste before assembly to seal the joint and provide a large contact area.

Table D.3   Acceptable materials for bonding

Equipment or Structure	Aluminium Strap	Tinned Copper Strap
Stainless Steel	Zinc plated washer	Direct
Aluminium	Direct	Aluminium washer
Steel	Direct	Direct
Copper	Zinc plated washer	Direct

(vi)   Bonding of structure
        The structure should be constructed to form a continuous RF tight screen with all parts of the structure at true earth potential. This requirement is met with either all steel welded, or all aluminium welded construction. Rivetted aluminium, and steel / aluminium composite structures, whether welded or rivetted, may not meet the requirements and might need bonding straps across the joints. The bonding straps should be concentrated near the corners of plates and be welded at both sides of the joint. Composite steel / aluminium structures need to be bonded across the rivetted joints. The bonding

straps should be aluminium or steel / aluminium exothermic welded material. In the case of aluminium bonding straps, the connection to the steel should be sealed against moisture ingress and remain visible for inspection. Alternatively, an easily replaceable sealing system may be used, e.g. heat shrink sleeving or tubing. Bonding is particularly important for mast structures, which may have a high degree of coupling with high frequency (HF) whip antennae.

(vii) All cabling which enters the structure from a high interference open deck area, e.g. close to transmitting or radar aerials, should ideally be run in metal conduit or be screened above deck. The screen or conduit should be earthed at the point of entry from the open deck, if possible by a 360° connection. Bonding joints should be watertight and protected from corrosion.

(viii) The precise earthing requirements for screened cables cannot be defined for all cases in advance and some site testing will sometimes be necessary to achieve the best arrangement. However the following guidelines should be followed.
(a) Power cables (a.c. and d.c) — Earthed at both ends or as near to the ends as possible. Intermediate earths may be necessary and may already be unavoidably present.
(b) Audio and very low frequency — Earthed at one end.
(c) RF — Where the cable is less than 1/8th wavelength long at the highest frequency of the interference spectrum, earthed at one end. For longer lengths the cable should be earthed at both ends and, if necessary, at frequent regular intervals, 1/8th wavelengths, along its length.

(ix) Spare pairs.
Where spare pairs exist in multi-cable runs or within multicore cables they should normally be isolated and taped back at each end. Alternatively it may be possible to achieve a better EMC environment by connecting them in parallel with pairs already in use. Earthing of spare pairs at one or both ends is not normally advisable but may be appropriate in particular cases.

(7)   Filters

To reduce the level of the transmission of EMI from the source to the sensitive equipment filters may be employed. However, inline filters are generally large, expensive and of doubtful value below 100 kHz but above this frequency the following considerations are valid.

(i) Power supplies
Filters should be installed as close to the input terminals of the equipment as possible except in the case where the power supply enters a screened compartment when the filter should be installed at the point of cable entry. Alternatively in this case the cable may be run through continuous metallic conduit which is bonded at the point of entry to the compartment, and a properly screened and bonded filter fitted at the input terminals of the equipment.

(ii) Signal cables
As a general rule a low pass filter and limiting diode will remove HF and pulse interference but additional selective filters may be required to suit individual equipments. However, care should be taken to ensure that any effective added capacitance does not affect the character of the wanted signals, e.g. pulse slope.

(iii) Connection plugs carrying inbuilt in-line filters are now available but tend to be expensive. Consideration should be given at an early design stage as to their incorporation in system cabling, so that, if need be, alternative methods may be adopted.

(iv) Fibre optic cable techniques and the use of optic isolators are becoming increasingly available and may be of value in solving difficult EMC problems. However, the art is still at an early stage of development and it is premature to give any general advice for such applications.

(8)   Power supply arrangements

(i) When designing a power supply arrangement to supply sensitive or interference producing equipment, consideration should be given to an isolating transformer, with an earthed metallic screen between windings, and suitably placed in the distribution system. It is desirable that power supplies to a screened compartment are taken through such a transformer located on, or in, the compartment boundary wall.

(ii) On power systems where convertors of large rating are incorporated, it may not be feasible to suppress harmonics generated by the convertors at source. In order to attenuate these effects on sensitive equipment, consideration should be given to motor generator sets placed in the distribution system to supply such equipment. The motor generator sets should be sited in a separate screened compartment, care being taken to ensure adequate separation of input and output cabling.

D.5   Radio / radar antenna systems

Transmitting antennae are likely to be the most powerful sources of radiated HF energy, whilst receiving antennae are among the most sensitive sensors of RF energy. Therefore great care must be taken, not only in the positioning of the various antennae, but in the design of the feeder runs between the antennae and associated equipment.

Antenna installations should meet the requirements of The Merchant Shipping (Radio Installations) Regulations 1980, The Merchant Shipping (Navigational Equipment) Regulations 1984 and the Home Office's Code of Practice for Ships Wire Antenna Systems for Radio Telegraphy Transmissions MPT 1270. (See Part 2, 1.3 and 5.5).

(1)   Antenna siting considerations

Consistent with keeping the feeder losses to a minimum the antenna layout design should be based on arranging for maximum separation between antennae. Desirable minimum separations are as follows:

(i) High and medium frequency (HF / MF) transmitting antennae should be separated as far from each other as practicable. Special care should be taken to ensure that there is maximum separation between transmitting and receiving antennae. Receiving antennae should be separated from each other by 5 metres where practicable.

(ii) Very high and ultra high frequency (VHF / UHF) transmitting antennae should be separated from each other by 3 metres or mounted on the same vertical axis with a separation of 1 metre. Where several VHF systems are installed, the receiving antennae should be separated from each other by 1 metre, and from transmitting antennae by 6 metres, or, preferably mounted co-axially and separated by 1 metre. However, for single equipment installations it is usual to make use of transmit / receive equipment using a single antenna.

Long wire ropes and stays if earthed at one end form very effective antennae which will absorb and re-radiate RF energy.

Such wire ropes and stays should be divided, by the use of insulators, into a number of non-resonant sections of varying lengths, the last section should be earthed at deck level. In the case of stays, the first section should bonded to the mast. See also BS 1597 and BS 5260.

(2)   Navaid antennae

Decca, Loran and satellite navigation equipment can be heavily affected by EMI picked up at the antennae and therefore some priority should be given to antenna location at the design stage. OMEGA equipment can be expected to tolerate a signal to noise ratio of 1:1 and because of the frequency and inherent make up of the OMEGA signal, antenna siting is not normally a severe problem as far as EMI is concerned.

(3)   Satellite terminal antennae

Satellite terminal antennae should be mounted as high as possible, clear of obstructions and away from potential sources of EMI, e.g. transmitting or radar antennae.

(4)   Active receiving antennae

These antennae have greatly eased the problem of arranging the distribution of antennae and should be seriously considered even for retrofit action since the problem of aerial gathered EMI is also reduced. However, their performance may be seriously affected by moderate field strengths from the transmitter causing the amplifier to overload with consequent clipping and resulting in a high degree of harmonic distortion in the output signal. Some improvement can be achieved by increasing the separation between the antennae.

(5)   Feeder considerations

(i) Feeder cables may re-radiate causing EMI, but in all cases will conduct EMI picked up from nearby sources back into the interior of the ship towards the sensitive equipment. Therefore, the screens of all feeders should be earthed at the point of entry from weatherdecks. The earth strap should be on the outside and kept as short as possible. Where unscreened feeder cable is used along open decks and exposed to radar or high energy emitting sources, it should be enclosed in electrically continuous metal conduit or metal trunking earthed at the point of entry from the open deck.

(ii) Cables carrying peak pulses exceeding 100 W should be spaced not less than 300 mm from all other cables.

(iii) In the case of HF and MF transmitters the aerial tuning unit (ATU) should be located as close as practicable to the antenna base. As far as is practicable the use of a coaxial feeder between the ATU and the transmitter terminals is desirable.

(iv) Grouping and separation of feeder cables should be in accordance with D.4(2). Solid metallic sheathed coaxial cables form a special case when used at frequencies above 30 MHz. These need not be separated into receiving and transmitting groups. They may be bundled together but should be separated from all other cables by at least 50 mm. Where this separation cannot be maintained the feeder should be run in metal conduit each section of which is bonded to earth.

Careful consideration should be given to long wire ropes and stays which, if earthed at one end, form very effective antennae capable of absorbing and re-radiating RF energy.

INDEX

NOTE: All references appear in Part 3 unless stated otherwise.

210

219

220

O

225